THE Butterflies
OF BERKSHIRE, BUCKINGHAMSHIRE AND OXFORDSHIRE

by Jim Asher

Pisces
PUBLICATIONS

Published by Pisces Publications
for Butterfly Conservation

BUTTERFLY CONSERVATION

with financial assistance from

ENGLISH NATURE

NORTHMOOR TRUST

First published by Pisces Publications 1994. Pisces Publications is the imprint of the Nature Conservation Bureau Limited.

British Library-in-Publication Data.
A catalogue record for this book is available from the British Library.

ISBN 1 874357 02 1

Designed and produced by The Nature Conservation Bureau Limited, 36 Kingfisher Court, Hambridge Road, Newbury, Berkshire, RG14 5SJ.

Printed by Information Press, Oxford.

Cover photograph: Pearl-bordered fritillary on a common spotted-orchid.

CONTENTS

FOREWORD

UNTIL JOINING the Upper Thames Branch of Butterfly Conservation in 1982, my interest in butterflies had been pursued, I am sorry to say, rather haphazardly. However, I was quickly introduced to the joys of informed butterfly observation and recording and, much to my surprise, received an acknowledgement in Caroline and David Steel's *Butterflies of Berkshire, Buckinghamshire and Oxfordshire* of 1985.

A further look at the acknowledgements in that book shows one of the names to be that of Jim Asher. In 1985, Jim became Branch Chairman and determined that Caroline and David's work should be continued and extended. Thus, in 1987, our atlas project was born. Six years later, with the help of over 350 recorders, we surpassed our original goal by obtaining detailed records for all parts of the three counties. Such a major task required many skills: firstly, charismatic leadership to inspire the recording effort required, secondly, the technical expertise to use computers to handle and present the data, thirdly, the knowledge of our butterflies to interpret the data into this easily readable book and, finally, the sheer determination to keep going over six long years. Almost single-handedly, Jim has brought all these skills to bear and it is only right that this magnificent work should stand witness to his effort. Furthermore, the computerised recording system he developed is being adopted nationally by other branches of Butterfly Conservation.

Seldom before has such thorough work been carried out over such a large area. Already it has confirmed Caroline and David's suspicions that the high brown fritillary is extinct and there are no colonies of large tortoiseshell in our region. The continued decline of the marsh, pearl-bordered and small pearl-bordered fritillaries casts doubt on their long-term survival locally. On the good side, the westward spread of the Essex skipper and the characteristic rise and fall of the holly blue have been monitored in detail, whilst some unrecorded colonies of key species have been 'discovered'.

However, this achievement should be seen only as the start. Having now established a sound baseline for the status of butterflies in our region, the recording effort must continue to enable an up-to-date picture to be kept available. Allied to this must go research into the ecological requirements of our threatened species, education of the public, landowners and our policy-makers, and active conservation work.

I hope that this Atlas gives you much pleasure and inspires you to become active in the fight to save our wild butterflies and their habitats.

David Redhead
Chairman, Upper Thames Branch of Butterfly Conservation 1990–1993

ACKNOWLEDGEMENTS

I HAVE LONG HAD AN AMBITION to write a book on butterflies, illustrated with photographs, to try to convey to others my fascination with these magnificent insects and the special corners of the countryside that they occupy, and my concerns about the disappearance of so many butterflies from our increasingly developed landscape.

Like some other enthusiasts of my age, my interest in butterflies was sparked off by the set of picture cards on British Butterflies issued by Brooke Bond in their tea packets around 1963. I collected and swapped cards with friends at school to complete not just one but two sets. This early interest was reinforced by the book *Observers Butterflies*, originally published in 1937 and only recently re-written and re-issued in a fully updated form.

I marvelled at that time over the variety of butterflies depicted and their evocative names – white admiral, Duke of Burgundy and purple emperor – but I was very envious indeed as a youngster in Scotland to realise how many were confined to southern England – a long way away if you have not been far south of Gretna Green! The card album (6d from the local shop) described how to catch butterflies and how to kill and pin them for display. I set about using a home-made net in the garden and on trips to the Ochil Hills and Sherrifmuir. My scope was limited, however, and a small tortoiseshell, a green-veined white, a small heath and a meadow brown looked very drab and small when finally pinned out, a sad comparison with live fluttering insects. I have clear recollections of hopelessly chasing after very dark brown butterflies in the hills – I think now it was probably Scotch argus, but I never did succeed in catching it except, more recently, on film.

My early enthusiasm dwindled but never fully disappeared. Some time after I had moved to Oxford in 1972, a colleague at work, well known in the local nature and walking community, Mr A. R. ('Mac') MacGill, suggested that I visit Bernwood – 'full of butterflies, a marvellous sight'. I am very much indebted to him for that introduction. Having recently bought a new SLR camera, a rather clumsy Praktica, I tried photographing marbled whites. The blurred and ill-composed results were awful, but it set me a challenge and I persevered with gradually improving results. Most of the photographs in this book were taken in the three counties using a reliable Pentax SLR camera, bought second-hand over 15 years ago.

I joined Butterfly Conservation and about a year later, in 1982, was invited to become a founder member of the new Upper Thames Branch set up by Caroline Steel. Caroline and David Steel were working on their book on butterflies of the three counties, published in 1985. When we decided in 1987 to improve on our knowledge of local butterflies by undertaking a much more detailed survey, I found myself in the thick of it. I am very grateful to Caroline for her part in setting up the project. Although she withdrew as an active organiser she has continued to show interest and to offer advice and records. The end result of this project, the book presented here, is a tribute to all who have helped in recording, to those who have contributed written material and to the branch committee for their continuous support, help and encouragement.

I am not an expert on butterflies, but I have learned more about them from the time I have spent looking closely at them. The more I have looked at and photographed them the more I realise how much there is still to discover. There are real experts whose knowledge of their behaviour and requirements is far above mine and some of their imparted knowledge is woven into this book. I only hope I have done them justice. I hope too that this book will encourage its readers to look more closely at these fascinating insects.

Contributors

I am grateful to the following for contributing some specialist material for this book: Nick Bowles on the chalkhill blue, Des Sussex on the silver-studded blue, Mike Wilkins on the M40 compensation area and Gary Roberts for notes on the black hairstreak reserve.

Financial assistance

Acknowledgements are gratefully given to the following for their generous financial support to the atlas project and/or publication of this book:

Berkshire County Council
Buckinghamshire County Council
Mr Denis Burroughes
Mr Robin Carr
English Nature

Middle-Thames Natural History Society
Milton Keynes Parks Trust Ltd
The Northmoor Trust
Oxfordshire County Council

Recorders

Andy Heryet, Atlas Coordinator of *Birds of Oxfordshire*, provided valuable advice and guidance in the early stages of setting up the butterfly survey of the three counties.

Thanks are due also to John Campbell at the Oxfordshire County Museum, Julian Scott at the Buckinghamshire County Museum, Mike Fuller of the Wiltshire butterfly mapping scheme, Sally Scott-White of the Wiltshire Biological Records Centre and Guy Meredith, Butterfly Conservation, Gloucestershire, for exchanging valuable records.

Butterfly Conservation is grateful to all of the following people who have given so much of their own time to participate in the survey and have provided records of butterfly sightings.

Martin Albertini
Danny Alder
Ted Ambrose
John Andrews
Denise Asher
John, Kirsty and Robert Asher
Mrs E. Ashley
Mrs Enid Atkins
Barry Auster
Catherine Ayres
T. Baker
R. Ballantyne
Frank Banyard
Barbara Barker
D. Barker
Martin Barker
Mrs Doreen E. Barnes
Niki Barrett
Mrs Eve Barry
Mrs Bayliss
Revd Alan E. Bean
Ron and Jaci Beaven
Brian T. Bennett
Dr M.J. Bennett
Alan Birch
P. Blackford
Charlie E. Blake
Mr and Mrs Malcolm Bodley
Mr J.T. Patrick Boston
F.C. Bover
Colin Bowler
Nick Bowles
Paul Bowyer
Sue Brawn
Glyn Bridge
Catherine Briggs
Eric D. Britnell
K. Broad
A.R. Broodbank
Elizabeth Brodie
Dick Brown
Paul Browning
Malcolm Brownsword
Revd P. Bugg
Richard and Caroline Bullock
E. Burden
Denis A. Burroughes
Phyl and Fred Butcher
Robin Buxton
Frances A. Cameron
John Campbell
Peter T. Carr
Mrs G. Cartwright
Peter Casselden

H.M. Cator
D. Chandler
Mr and Mrs I. Chisholm
Mrs R.A. Chisholm
Gareth Clare
Bernard Clark
B.D. Clews
B.J. and S.A. Clift
Mick J. Clist
Mr M.R. Cochrane
Mrs Mary Cockin
Dr A.D. Cole
Barry and Jennifer Collett
Barry Cooper
Chris Coppock
Mrs J. Cornock
Mrs W. de Coverly
Mrs Sue Cowdy
Peter Creed
Mr R.S. Crickman
Maureen Cross
Miss Pat Crutch
Jan Culf
Elizabeth Cull
Mr F. Curd
Sheila and John Dally
Elizabeth Daniel
Martin Daniel
David Darby
Ray F. Darke
Lt Col Richard Dauncey
A.R. Davey
E. Dean
D.H. Dell
Graham Dennis
Linda Dobbs
Eric and Sheila Dunford
Ivan Dunn
T. Dyer
Graham R.S. Elcombe
Ian Evans
S.J. Farnsworth
David Ferguson
John Field
Mrs Geraldine B. Fisher
R.S.R. Fitter
Mike A. Flemming
Mrs P.L. Ford
Dr R.T.V. Fox
Jim French
Mrs Margaret Furniss
Paul and Hilary Gallagher
Charles Garrett-Jones
Joyce Gay

Dr A.M. George
J Gibbings
Mrs N.M. Gibson
Graham Giles
Mrs Kim Gillson
Mrs Anstace Gladstone
Marcus J. Goddard
R.J. Godden
Mr F.W. Golby
Betty Gomm
Joe Gomme
David Gore
Mrs Enid M. Gow
Mrs M. Grant
I.J. Gray
E.E. Green
J.D. Griffiths
Mr and Mrs Mark Griffiths
Simon Grove
Peter Hall
Jeremy Halls
Mrs Pat Hanson
Janis Harman
Miss F.E. Harvey
Bill Havers
Paul D.G. Hayter
W.F. Head
Mrs R. Held
John E. Henley
Colin Herbert
Greg Herbert
Mrs Elizabeth Hewitt
G.E. Higgs
Simon Hill
Paul and Karalie Hillyer
Siriol Hinchliffe
Mary Hockey
Brian Hodge
Mr D.G. Hodge
M.E. Hodges
Mr Stuart Hodges
Simon Holden
Brian Horner
Mrs Beryl Horswell
Dave Horton
T.M. Hotten
Mrs P.A. Hudson
Ann-Marie Hulme
Mrs Jeannine Hunt
Bob Hurst
Roger Hussey
J. and P. Illenden
C.M. Jackson-Houlson
Miss Rosemary Jeffrey

David Jennings
Mrs G.J. Jewell
A. Johnson
Mrs H.R. Jones
Mick Jones
Mrs Janet Keene
Roger Kemp
Darryl Kempster
Gerry M. Kendall
Stuart Kershaw
Jon King
Judith Kingwill
Mr Kittoe
Andrew Knight
Wendy Knight
Peter Lack
Graham B. Langley
R. Lansdown
Antony Leaf
Richard Lewington
Mike Lewis
V. Lewis
Derek Longe
Mrs D. Lorch
Mrs Joy Lowther
A.J. Lucas
Nik Luker
Heather Lund
Ken Lunnon
Gordon A. Maclean
Mrs J.L. Manning
Pat M. Mansfield
Helen Marcan
H.T. Marlow
Trish and Alan Marshall
T.F. and V. Marshall
Peter Martin
Roger Maskell
Ian Mathieson
Lin Matthews
Roy Maycock
R. Mayhew
K. McDonnell
Neil McMillan
Reg Mead
Kathleen Meadows
M.G. Meardon
Mary Melluish
Guy Meredith
J. Middleton
Revd H.G. Miles
Don Miller
John Miller
Liz Miller

Mrs B. Miller
Mr D. Moll
Mrs R.P. Monk
Gareth Morgan
I.B. Morris
Mrs Pat Morris
Monty Mortimer
Mick Munns
Trevor Munns
Dr John Murray
Mrs Katherine Murray
Miss A. Neal
Iris Newbery
Philip Noon
John Norledge
Mrs Barbara North
K.I. Norton
Mrs G.E. Noton
A.G.H. Osborn
Mrs W.H. Osborne
Dr T.G. Osmond
Daphne Owen
G. Owen
Jerry Page
Mrs D.C. Palmer
Roger Payne
E. Pegler
Mrs B.K. Phillips
Peter J. Pool
K. Porter
J.A. Prince
Mrs Tricia Pritchard

Mr R. Radford
Mrs Margaret Randall
R.A.S. Ratcliffe
Tony Rayner
David L. Redhead
Mrs Joan Rhoades
Ivor Rhymes
Claude Rivers
Gary M. Roberts
David Robertson
T.S. Robertson
Miss T.F. Robinson
Michael Root
Miss J. Royston
C.H. and J. Sabin
Julie Saunders
C.M. Sayers
Roy W.H. Scroggs
Mrs Elizabeth Seager
A.G. Searle
Mrs B. Sewell
Ann Shackle
R. and S. Sheppard
A.J. Simpson
Mr R.G. Simpson
Chris Sinclair
D.E. Sitch
Alan C. Smith
Mr B.W. Smith
Mrs Linda Smith
M. Smith
Tony Smith

Mrs W.E. Smith
Wally Smith
Mrs C. Snook
Mrs Jenny C. Southern
Mrs Shirley Spencer
Miss A. and P. Stafford
Barry Staines
Peter E. Standley
Caroline Steel
Paul Stenton
Peter J. Stevens
Mrs J.R. Steward
G.J. Stewart
B. Stickland
Mr J.R. Stockbridge
Malcolm Story
Des Sussex
Paul Swan
Andy Swash
N.S. Thom
E. Thompson
P.L. Thompson
Gordon Thornton
J.A. and R. Timberlake
L.R. Tipping
Mrs Jean Tuck
Simon and Joanne Tuck
Adrian Tucker
Mrs G.W. Tucker
Roger Vergine
Margaret Vickery
John Wakeley

A. Walker
Peter R.P. Walton
Rod Ward
Mr Paul R. Watkins
Dr A.B. Watts
Mick Watts
Chris Webster
Carl Welch
Mrs S. Welsberg
Malcolm Wemyss
S.P.B. West
Ian Weston
H.F. Wheate
Steve Whitby
David J. White
Mr Ard Whitlock
J.C. Wickham
Miss M.R.T. Wigan
Brian Wildridge
Tim Wildridge
Mike A. Wilkins
D.E.D. Wilkinson
Mrs Linda Wisbey
Mrs V. Withall
Becky Woodell
A. Woods
Mr Edward V. Wright
Mrs Pat K. Wright
Ted Wright
Dr G. Wynne-Thomas
D.R. Young

I would also like to thank Mike Wilkins for entering data from many of the submitted recording forms into the computer system in preparation for sorting.

This project has taken a large amount of my time and that of my family. I am very grateful to Denise and to John, Kirsty and Robert for their help with recording and for the years of support that they have given – their enduring patience has been worn thin too often. They have earned the right to claim a share of the credit for this project and I dedicate the book to them.

Jim Asher
April 1994

INTRODUCTION

BUTTERFLIES occupy a special place in most people's affections. Their bright colours and movement in flight add an extra dimension to the pleasures of gardens and the countryside and they are a widely recognised symbol of sunshine and summer. To the natural historian, they provide a simple indicator of the natural wealth of a site. Their colours and complex wing patterns are fascinating in themselves and give inspiration to the artist. The butterfly is frequently used as a powerful image of nature in publicity and advertising. But they also have a negative side – two of our butterflies are unwelcome pests of the cabbage garden. Ask the average person in the street to name two butterflies and the most likely replies will be 'red admiral' and 'cabbage white'.

Britain has a long history of butterfly watching, as an integral part of a national interest in the natural world. The first book to describe butterflies was published (in Latin) in 1634, by Sir Theodore de Mayerne, physician to Charles I. This work was followed over the years by many more, as interest in natural history grew. There are probably more books on natural history, and on butterflies in particular, published in Britain than in all other countries put together. Perhaps this is because our changeable climate gives us a sharper appreciation of sunshine and the indicators of summer. We have numerous butterflies, but not in such large numbers that we take them for granted. They also fit well with our other great national interests, gardening and a love of the countryside.

The traditional clouds of butterflies in our country lanes and meadows are becoming a fading memory of the past, as changes in our environment take their toll. A complaint frequently voiced by many older people is that butterflies are nowhere as common as they were in their childhood. In this sense, butterflies act as a symbolic (and indeed real) indicator of the decline in the natural wealth of the landscape. The butterfly provides a flagship for the cause of conservation in its wider aims of protecting the biodiversity of our planet in an age of unprecedented pressure on its resources. There is firm evidence to show that efforts focused on the conservation of butterflies often lead to benefits for many other insects, plants and animals, in many cases less obvious but just as endangered.

The main objective of this book is to describe the butterflies found in Berkshire, Buckinghamshire and Oxfordshire, illustrated with photographs mostly taken in this local area. The distribution map shown with each species is based on the results of a thorough survey of the area made over the six years from 1987 to 1992. The maps highlight the present status of species and point to a few expansions, but to many more dramatic declines and a strong message that conservation work is needed. Later chapters discuss the habitats and management work required to protect our local butterfly species.

What are butterflies?

Butterflies are part of a very large and successful class, the insects. Like all other insects, their bodies have three segments: the head, the thorax and the abdomen. They have six legs and two pairs of wings, attached to the thorax. The wings are not interconnected, but work together to provide thrust and lift when the butterfly is in flight, with a complex beating and twisting movement, acting rather like sails. The large area of the wings gives them a fluttering and erratically changing flight. The largest of the British butterflies, the swallowtail, has a wingspan of up to 93 mm; the largest found in this local area is the purple emperor, with a wingspan of up to about 90 mm. The smallest is the small blue with a wingspan of as little as 16 mm.

The butterflies form a small group of families, referred to formally as the Rhopalocera, within a much larger order of insects, the Lepidoptera, which includes the very much more numerous moths. There are only about 60 species of butterfly in this country (the exact number depends on whether occasional migrant species are included), compared to about 2,500 species of moth. Britain is unusual in naming butterflies as a separate group of the Lepidoptera. This distinction was not made in the earliest British books on insects, which referred to moths simply as nocturnal butterflies. In many other European countries, the butterflies and moths together are given one collective name, for example 'papillons' in France, 'farfalli' in Italy and 'mariposas' in Spain, although in many of these countries a distinction is made between day- and night-flying species (for example, 'papillons de jour' and 'papillons de nuit' in France). In fact, there are more differences between some families of butterfly species than there are between some butterfly and some moth species. In Britain, the moth has an undeserved reputation for being slightly sinister and suffers a much lower popularity rating, partly because of the peculiar way it flies around lights at night and partly perhaps because of the ravages of clothes moth caterpillars. This book, however, concentrates on those species traditionally known in Britain as 'the butterflies'.

The scientific name for this insect order, 'Lepidoptera', derives from the Greek for 'scale-wings' and refers to the distinctive construction of the wings. They consist of an array of minute scales attached to a double-skinned framework. A microscope reveals that the coloured patterns on the wings are formed by a mosaic made up of a very large number of small coloured scales fixed to the structural network of the wing.

In the males of many butterfly species, some of the scales, normally on the forewings, are modified to secrete sophisticated scents, made of substances called *pheromones*. The scent, released from these *androconial* scales when the wings are vibrated, attracts the female of the species. If she is available for mating, she responds by releasing scent, usually from her abdomen, in a courtship ritual which consolidates the male's attentions. The two antennae projecting from the head of the butterfly are used as organs of smell. The ends of the antennae are clubbed (the term Rhopalocera means 'club-horn'). Moths use scent in a similar way and in many moth species the highly developed feather-like antennae of the male can detect and locate a female at a distance of over a kilometre.

The large compound eyes provide almost all-round vision. Individual cells in the eyes are linked so that if nearby movement generates signals at the same time in several cells, an instinctive response triggers take-off into flight. Therefore, if you want to approach closely to a butterfly, you must avoid sudden movement particularly across its line of sight.

The adult butterfly draws energy from two external sources, sunlight and liquid fuel. It can fly only when its body temperature is high enough. It is therefore seldom seen when it is cool and overcast and takes cover to roost in early evening when the sun drops low in the sky. Generally, most species will not fly unless the temperature is above about 13°C on a sunny day or above about 17°C when it is overcast. They tend not to fly in windy conditions, unless the temperature is relatively high. Most species will bask, spreading their wings to face directly into the sun to increase their temperature. On very hot days, many butterflies seem to disappear, as if for a siesta, around midday. They dive into the undergrowth to avoid the danger of desiccation, but reappear in late afternoon when it is cooler.

Solar energy is supplemented by feeding from nectar-rich flowers, which provide a high-sugar and high-protein diet. Liquid is drawn in through a double tube, called a *proboscis* (sometimes referred to as the tongue), which is held coiled up under the head when not feeding. Some butterflies, especially tree-canopy species, feed also on the sticky honeydew deposits left by aphids. Red admirals sometimes feed from the sugary sap oozing from a wound on a tree. They also frequent the orchard, along with commas (and wasps), drinking the fermenting juices from rotting fruit pecked open by birds. The intense nectaring habit of those species that hibernate as adults provides stocks of body fats to maintain them through the winter.

Mating can deplete male butterflies of salts. Some species compensate for this, particularly in hot weather, by drinking from damp gravel or muddy patches and sometimes from animal droppings on the ground (see the descriptions of the chalkhill blue and the purple emperor) – behaviour associated more with tropical species. On dry surfaces, they can exude droplets of fluid to dissolve salts and then draw them in again using the proboscis.

Life cycle of the butterfly

In common with other insects, the butterfly goes through a sequence of different forms during its development. Butterflies have four distinct stages of development, starting with the egg (or ovum), from which the larva, commonly known as the caterpillar, hatches. The caterpillar is a feeding machine, designed for growth.

The fully grown caterpillar turns into a pupa, sometimes known as a chrysalis. The butterfly forms inside the pupal case, emerging as an adult. This remarkable transformation from a drab and sometimes ugly caterpillar, via the pupa, to a beautifully coloured flying machine contributes greatly to our fascination with these insects. The adults mate, often after complex courting rituals, and the female goes off to find suitable foodplants on which eggs are laid to complete the cycle.

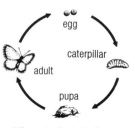

Life-cycle of a butterfly

3

The details of the time spent in each stage of the cycle, the stage at which hibernation occurs and the strategies used for concealment differ in detail from one species to another, but there are many general similarities. Although the adult butterflies are obvious where they occur, the immature stages are small and/or well-concealed and few people have the opportunity to see them, unless they know where to look. The sequence of photographs below illustrates the key features in the life-cycle of one species, the white admiral.

The sequence starts with the egg, shown here photographed under a microscope, laid near to the edge of a leaf of its foodplant, honeysuckle. The egg is attached to the leaf by a spot of adhesive material, similar to the silk-like excretions used at later stages. At this magnification, the hairs on the leaves appear as spines. The diameter of the egg is about the same as that of a dressmaker's pin, and it is patterned with cell markings and spines.

The caterpillar forms within the egg and hatches one to two weeks later. In many species, the caterpillar must first eat part of the egg shell, which contains essential nutrients. It then starts to eat from the tip of the leaf, but uses the central vein for resting. It deposits its own droppings on the central vein to assist with camouflage at this early stage.

The caterpillars of all butterflies have three pairs of true legs toward the head end. They also have four pairs of 'pro-legs' mid-way along the body and a pair of claspers at the back end, which are not true limbs, but simply projections from the body used to grip, and assist it in walking. The head has a complex system of jaws used for rapid food intake.

Caterpillars, as with all stages of an insect, take their shape from the tough outer skin – they have no skeleton. This skin can accommodate only limited growth, so the caterpillar has to develop a new skin and shed the old one at several stages in its lifetime. It stops feeding, attaches its tail end to a stem with silk and waits while a new skin develops inside the old. When it is ready, it pushes off the old head capsule and squirms its way out of the old skin, leaving it behind like a small wrinkled wrapper. It takes an hour or two for the new skin and jaws to harden before the caterpillar can start feeding again. There are

normally five or six such stages (known as *instars*) in the life of a caterpillar. Caterpillars do not breathe in the way we do, with complex lungs. Air simply diffuses through narrow tubes distributed along their bodies, called spiracles, without muscular effort.

Caterpillar metabolism depends strongly on temperature. As the temperature drops, their activity decreases rapidly. As autumn approaches, the white admiral caterpillar prepares for hibernation. It first fixes a partly eaten leaf to the stem of the plant, so that it does not fall into the ground litter with the other leaves in late autumn, and therefore avoids exposing itself to the risk of being eaten by a ground predator. It then spins silk threads between the edges of the leaf. As they dry and shrink, the threads pull the edges of the leaf together, forming a pocket, called a *hibernaculum*, to provide concealment for the winter.

The following spring, the caterpillar, withered and brown, matching the colour of the dead leaf, becomes active again, sheds its old skin and starts feeding. As it grows, the stages become successively larger and more aggressive looking. The bright green colour of the upperside mimics that of the leaves, while the sides are the same maroon colour as the plant stems. It has a double row of branched spines along its back. When disturbed, it arches its back, displaying the spines prominently to drive off a potential threat.

The fully grown caterpillar, about 35 mm long, stops feeding and prepares to pupate. It first spins a pad of silk on the stem of the plant. It then attaches itself by its tail end to the pad from which it hangs upside-down in a characteristic J-shape. Some other species of caterpillar attach themselves with a girdle of silk thread round the body to hold them firmly against a leaf or twig; others form a cocoon of leaves and silk inside which they form a pupa. Inside the caterpillar skin, the pupal skin forms. After 1 or 2 days, the pupa breaks open the caterpillar skin and begins to work it up its body with a strong wriggling motion. As the old skin reaches the top, the newly emerging pupa wriggles much more strongly and with a deft movement, during which it grips the old skin with a fold in its body, works its tail end out and attaches it to the silk pad, allowing the old skin to drop off.

The pupa is attached to the silk by a device called a *cremaster* which looks, under a microscope, like the hooked part of a Velcro fastener – nature invented this tangle of tiny hooks long before man did – which hold it firmly in place. Over the following hours, the shape and colour of the pupa develop, until it looks like a wet bird dropping hanging from the plant stem. The wet effect is enhanced by shiny golden patches; the name *chrysalis*, sometimes used to describe this stage, comes from the Greek word for gold – *chrysos* – after these patches which appear on the pupae of some butterfly species.

It takes 2–3 weeks for the butterfly to form inside the pupa. During this time there is a dramatic reorganisation of the cell structure, to convert a former eating machine into a flying, mating and egg-producing machine. Towards the end of this period, the colours fade and gradually the strong black colour of the butterfly wings with their white markings show through. Shortly before the butterfly emerges, the lines around the abdomen show signs of stretching, until the skin splits from the bottom end, where the head is, and the butterfly pushes its way out. The head appears first, followed by the proboscis, and then the antennae. With a final struggle, it pulls itself fully out and hangs by its legs from the empty pupal case.

At this stage, the wings are still folded and limp. Gradually, by pumping fluid into the wing cavities, they are stretched out to full size over a period of 5 to 10 minutes. During this time, it is very vulnerable to attack. Because its wings are limp, it cannot fly to escape. There is another risk. If there is a twig, stem or blade of grass in the way, the wings may be prevented from expanding fully and may become warped or folded. If this happens, the butterfly's flight may be severely disabled and it may not be viable.

After expanding its wings fully, the butterfly hangs quite motionless in the sun for about an hour, until the wings have hardened and become stiff enough for flight. It prepares to fly by first vibrating the wings to warm the flight muscles. A few minutes later, it flies off to nectar, to find a mate and restart the cycle.

The success of any generation is governed by the number of eggs that are laid, and subsequently by the number that develop through to adults. If there is prolonged cool or wet weather during the flying season, then mating and egg-laying may be severely restricted, resulting in a very poor population in the following generation. Such short-term weather factors have a significant impact on the numbers of butterflies seen.

The key features of the three counties

The three counties of Berkshire, Buckinghamshire and Oxfordshire form a compact block of varied countryside in the south Midlands of England. The main geographical features of this area are the broad chalk ridge of the Downs and Chilterns with a north-facing escarpment, intersected by the River Thames at the Goring Gap, and the broad Vales of Oxford and Aylesbury with heavy clay soils. The area is bounded by low limestone and ironstone hills to the north, the limestones of the Cotswolds to the west, the clay vale of Kennet to the south-west and the heaths bordering Hampshire and Surrey to the south and south-east. Within a small area, therefore, this block contains a very good mixture of geology and soil types, and a correspondingly rich variety of grassland, heathland and woodland types each with their own characteristic flora.

Different plants occupy different niches in the landscape. Some plants thrive on acid soils, others on alkaline soils. Some need dry, open conditions, others need sheltered and damp conditions. Butterflies, along with other insects, have evolved to take advantage of the different plants available and have developed their own specialised dependences on individual plant species and the locations in which they occur.

The combination of a particular type of vegetation, generally associated with the underlying geology of the soil, together with its situation in the local landscape is referred to as a 'habitat'. This area contains significant woodland (ranging from remnants of ancient deciduous woodland, scrub and high forest to forestry plantation – conifer, broad-leaved and mixed), dry and damp grassland and heathland habitats, with a rich variety of natural species of flora and fauna, some of which are nationally rare.

The broad mixture of habitat types in the three counties is reflected in the comparatively wide variety of butterfly species. A total of 48 butterfly species are recorded as breeding in this area, out of the national total of about 60, which is as high as any other equivalent area in Britain and higher than most. There is, however, no one site in the area at which all 48 species are recorded – although many common species are found almost everywhere, a significant number are restricted to particular habitats and will not breed outside these. This can be seen by comparing the distribution maps for white admiral and chalkhill blue, shown together on page 16. The former is a species of damp woodland and therefore found mainly in the low-lying clay-rich areas, whilst the latter is a species of dry grassland, restricted to the steep chalky slopes of the Downs and Chilterns. Their distributions reflect these very different habitats with no significant overlap in this area.

This region is, however, under increasingly intense pressure for development, because of its national position overlapping with the industrial heartland of the Midlands and the commuter belt around London. The area is intersected by major motorways (M1, M4, M40) and trunk roads (A4, A40, A34). There has been recent discussion about a new east–west motorway route passing Aylesbury and Oxford. Construction projects require that more and more sand and gravel is extracted. Towns in all three counties, for example Banbury, Aylesbury and Newbury, are scheduled for further expansion of both industry and housing. Industrial developments, with associated increases in demand for housing, shopping and leisure centres and golf courses, grow to dominate a formerly rural landscape.

Coupled with economic expansion and industrial development, there have been far-reaching changes in agricultural and forestry methods since the war. Intensification of agriculture, to make Britain self-sufficient, has resulted in removal of hedgerows, fertilisation of traditional meadows, drainage of ancient wetlands and application of large quantities of pesticides and herbicides to maximise food production.

Although some butterfly species can adapt to the resulting landscape changes, several of the more specialised ones are under threat and measures have to be taken to conserve them where they still survive. We are fortunate to live at a time when we can enjoy the benefits of modern industrial development and yet still have the opportunity to see some of these less common species. Their survival here cannot be taken for granted and without positive conservation strategies we risk losing them for our children and our grandchildren.

The key to conservation of butterfly species is to conserve the remnants of special habitat that they require for their survival. The current status of each individual species of butterfly in this local area and the management methods required to conserve their habitats are discussed in more detail later in this book.

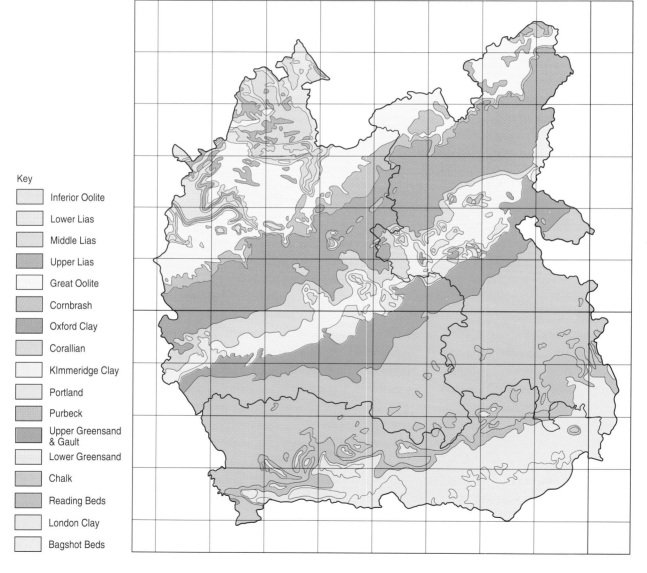

Key

Inferior Oolite

Lower Lias

Middle Lias

Upper Lias

Great Oolite

Cornbrash

Oxford Clay

Corallian

KImmeridge Clay

Portland

Purbeck

Upper Greensand & Gault

Lower Greensand

Chalk

Reading Beds

London Clay

Bagshot Beds

Butterfly Conservation

Butterfly Conservation was founded in 1968 as a national organisation with the aim of protecting our native butterflies and moths and their natural habitats. It has grown rapidly over the last few years, with a campaign to increase publicity and resources, to a membership of about 10,000 in 1993. Butterfly Conservation is now probably the largest insect conservation body in the world.

A network of 27 regional branches, covering most of the country, is active in carrying out most of the groundwork of the society, including active habitat management, detailed species recording and local studies of butterflies along with local publicity, education and fund-raising. The central organisation is responsible for coordination, major fund-raising and sponsorship, national surveys, research, conservation policies and large-scale educational initiatives.

The ultimate aim of the society is the restoration of a more balanced countryside, with populations of butterflies, moths and other wildlife returned to the profusion that we once enjoyed. Butterfly Conservation lobbies our decision-makers for change at a local and a national level, supporting efforts on a wider European scale to bring in real legislative controls to safeguard those species most at risk. It is recognised that this ultimate ideal has to be set against the other pressures on our society and economy, and the society actively seeks solutions that are practical and realistic.

Britain is not unique in having problems with loss of habitats and species and the local picture of human impact on the landscape is reflected on a worldwide scale. Butterfly Conservation also has an international perspective and is actively improving links with corresponding conservation bodies elsewhere in Europe and worldwide.

The Upper Thames Branch of Butterfly Conservation was founded in 1982 with about 40 members and now has a membership of over 400. It covers the modern administrative counties of Berkshire, Buckinghamshire and Oxfordshire, which it shares with the longer-established local wildlife trust, the Berkshire, Buckinghamshire and Oxfordshire Naturalists' Trust (BBONT). Many local people with butterfly conservation interests are members of both. Butterfly Conservation assists BBONT with the development of management plans for butterflies on several of their reserves and in active conservation work, and also works with other local landowners to advise on and assist with active habitat management. Regular field meetings through the summer and evening talks during the winter provide an opportunity for members to learn more about butterflies and their needs.

In practice, the work of a voluntary body such as Butterfly Conservation is reliant on its membership and resources. The society is always keen to welcome new members and is open to offers of practical and financial assistance to help it achieve its objectives (see page 136 for address).

UPPER THAMES
BUTTERFLY ATLAS
PROJECT

I N 1987, the Upper Thames Branch of Butterfly Conservation embarked on a project to map out the distribution of all local butterfly species on a grid of 2 km squares over the three counties of Berkshire, Buckinghamshire and Oxfordshire. A five-year recording period from 1987 to 1991 was initially chosen, but was subsequently extended to include 1992. This chapter describes the approach to the task, some of the problems encountered and the methods used to achieve the objectives set.

In 1985, Caroline and David Steel published *Butterflies of Berkshire, Buckinghamshire and Oxfordshire*. This was based on data accumulated from casual observations of butterflies by some 65 individual recorders and local recording centres over the ten years 1975–1984. The coverage was such, however, that distributions could only be shown at the level of 10 km grid squares.

A finer coverage is necessary to reflect the status of individual colonies, particularly for threatened species. A 2 km grid square, known as a *tetrad*, gives a good compromise between achievable coverage and matching to individual colonies. Although *An Atlas of Oxfordshire Butterflies* (Knight and Campbell , 1982) gave data on a tetrad basis for pre-1960, 1960–79 and post-1979 records, it included only a fraction of the 2 km squares covering the county.

It was felt that thorough mapping on this more detailed scale was required over a short period, to obtain comprehensive and up-to-date information at a time of increasingly rapid decline of habitats and increasing demands for data to tackle local planning issues. Unless records of important species are recent, they are generally discounted at the planning stage.

Data collection

The three counties are covered by 1,560 tetrads (the few squares outside this area which have an overlap of less than 5% with the three counties have been ignored). To try to achieve comprehensive coverage on this scale, and over a five year period, presented a major challenge, even for such a well-populated region (it is a far greater challenge, nigh impossible, in remote and sparsely populated areas such as Highland Scotland). Merely relying on the casual records returned by a few dedicated recorders alone was not enough; a more directed and positive approach was required.

A campaign was mounted, initially within Upper Thames Branch, to encourage members to record the butterflies they saw on visits or walks around the local countryside. An information sheet, based at first on that for the Oxfordshire bird atlas recording scheme, was devised, giving instructions on how to record and what areas to try to cover. A recording sheet was designed and circulated to collect data on site location, date of visit and butterflies seen, with a simple classification of numbers seen. This evolved later to revised forms for site and casual recording designed to comply with proposed new national recording standards.

The area was divided into 10 km Ordnance Survey grid squares. Individuals were approached to act as recording coordinators for their local squares, so as to direct local efforts towards complete coverage of each square. This was partially successful. Some very vigorous coordinators were recruited, who in some cases covered all 25 tetrads in their 10 km square either on their own or by organising a local network of helpers; some took on more than one 10 km square. For about a third of the 79 10 km squares no suitable volunteer was available and the survey depended on casual and later centrally directed recording.

Recommendations were made that sites representative of different habitats in each square should be visited at least four times through the season. In many tetrads, particularly in the agriculturally intensive Vales of Oxford and Aylesbury, there is precious little habitat of any obvious conservation value, other than a few footpaths, set-aside areas or roadside verges, and visits tended to be quickly completed.

At the edges of the area, some squares overlap with other counties. If more than 5% of a tetrad lay within one of the three counties, then the whole of that tetrad (including the parts outside the county boundary) was recorded in full.

One of the key species in the local area is the black hairstreak, at the south-west end of its peculiar range in Britain. From 1988, 'black hairstreak weekends' were organised to explore previously known and possible new sites for this elusive species. Meeting points were arranged at four sites where there were known to be established colonies. The idea was for recorders to become familiar with the butterfly's appearance, and then disperse to explore nearby sites where it was thought likely that there might be colonies.

Needless to say, the years between 1988 and 1991 proved to be very poor seasons for the black hairstreak. Very few were seen, and people became discouraged. A combination of cold June weather, three years running, and wet weather just when recorders went out to look for them, turned carefully laid plans upside-down and little progress was made. In 1992, no special arrangements were made and the species began to show up again! Consequently, the survey has had to rely mostly on 1987 and 1992 sightings for data on this species.

Data storage and analysis

Timely feedback to recorders of progress and updates on the coverage achieved were an essential key to maintaining momentum and motivation, and directing recording effort most effectively. Thus it was almost essential to use computer-based data collection and analysis. The data storage system, using software developed initially on a BBC microcomputer and later adapted for use on a PC, was specifically designed for fast and efficient data entry – time is the most valuable resource for any project.

Data were typed in to generate computer record files, partly with the help of other recorders with home computers, who were able to supply data in disk format, using the same data filing program. A few welcome helpers took on the task of entering data from the very large pile of recording sheets that accumulated in 1990, 1991 and 1992. These data files provided the raw data from which distribution maps and flight season diagrams were generated.

Feedback to recorders

Feedback to recorders was provided in various forms. An annual report was written on the progress to date with up-to-date maps of recorded squares and a few distribution maps of selected species, particularly if there was a topical context, for example the holly blue population explosion which occurred within the atlas recording period.

A recorders meeting was held each spring, to keep square coordinators up-to-date and to discuss tactics and slight changes in the format of recording forms, which evolved as the project proceeded. Coverage of the more poorly-recorded areas was organised. As a result of increasing momentum, the level of recording grew rapidly from a modest start in the first year. Below are maps of the squares recorded for each of the six years of the project.

Figure 1: Maps of squares recorded for 1987, 1988, 1989, 1990, 1991, 1992

Key: · 1–7 species
       • 8–15 species
       ● 16+ species

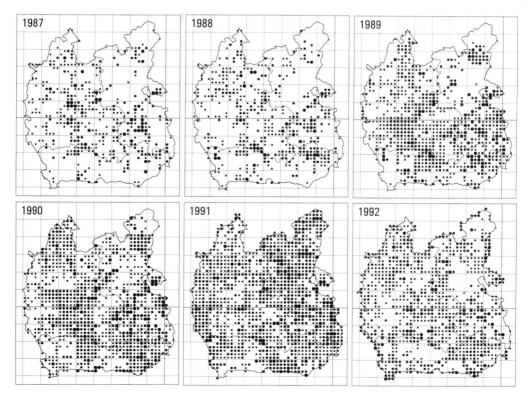

Feedback sheets for each 10 km square were printed each year for square coordinators and individual recorders to see which tetrads had been covered and which species had been recorded locally, and to draw attention to gaps in coverage. Each year, all recorders who sent in records received a copy of the annual report, new recording forms and their local 10 km square print-out sheets with requests to target specific squares.

Data from other sources, such as garden and churchyard surveys, data received from the local county museums record centres and casual records from correspondents, were also incorporated into the database.

Appeals were published in the local wildlife trust (BBONT) newsletter for data and recorders. In the last two years of the project, these appeals were directed at requesting data from well-defined named local areas where coverage was still very poor. As a result, some 50+ extra recorders joined the project. Cooperation with BBONT has been very good and useful exchanges of data have been made.

Even at the end of the fourth year, there were still some significant gaps in the coverage, particularly in north Buckinghamshire and north-east Berkshire. A map of unrecorded tetrads was distributed to highlight the empty spaces and effort was concentrated on these areas in 1991 and 1992. A 'help list' detailing specific villages/areas needing coverage was distributed through local meetings, BBONT, and other local groups. This resulted in a number of people offering to fill several of the gaps.

Further appeals were made in early 1991 in the local press and on local radio, mentioning under-recorded areas and resulting in a further crop of recorders and some new members for Butterfly Conservation. Branch members living in tetrads that remained unrecorded were individually approached and several collected local records in the last full year of recording.

Attempts were made to organise 'raiding parties' to record intensively in poorly covered areas. A small number of the most dedicated recorders undertook several day-long trips to such areas, covering up to 20 squares a day in hot sunshine, in response to pleas in 1991 and 1992. Some still have not forgiven the project for turning recording into an obsession for them!

Neighbouring Butterfly Conservation branches were approached to exchange data for those tetrads that overlap county boundaries and therefore branch boundaries – where recording tends to be weak.

The persistence paid off. In 1991 alone, records were collected from over 1,170 tetrads out of the total of 1,560. An extra year, 1992, was added, partly to allow a few missed or under-recorded squares to be visited and partly because in the first year (1987) only a limited amount of recording had been achieved. Over six years, an average of over five visits was made to each of the tetrad squares targeted. The average number of species recorded was almost 16 per tetrad. The database contains over 90,000 species sightings from about 17,000 visits, made by over 350 people. This must make it one of the most intensive local butterfly surveys in Britain. The distribution maps used in this book incorporate the results from this survey.

LEFT Figure 2: Cumulative distribution of records 1987–1992

Key:
- · 1–9 species
- ● 10–19 species
- ● 20+ species

RIGHT Figure 3: Distribution of key species records 1987–1992

Key:
- · 1 key species
- ● 2–4 key species
- ● 5+ key species

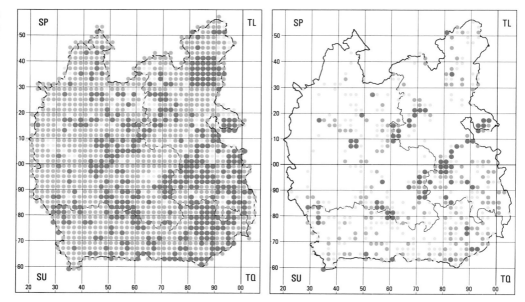

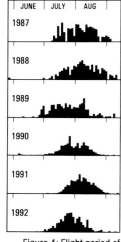

Figure 4: Flight period of the gatekeeper showing year to year variations

The coverage is illustrated in Figure 2, which shows the cumulative distribution of all records at the end of the final year, with the symbols coded to indicate number of species recorded in each tetrad; Figure 3 shows the number of 'key species' – localised and threatened species only (see Check list on p. 133) – that were recorded in each square. This shows that there are particular areas where there are higher concentrations of these key species.

The number of squares in which each species was recorded over the survey period is shown in the table. Although this does not provide a rigorous estimate of the true abundance of species, it provides a crude but simple indication of their relative status. This shows clearly the enormous variation in abundance between the most common species and our most threatened species.

From the same database, data were extracted on the flight season of each species, year by year. These showed significant variations in both the length and the mid-point of the seasons for several species, reflecting differences in seasonal weather. These tend to move together; 1989 and 1990 showed seasons some 5–15 days earlier for single-brooded species than 1987 and 1988. 1991 was more like 1988 than 1990. These variations are illustrated in Figure 4 which shows recorded frequency for the gatekeeper, for each year between 1987 and 1992.

One of the most valuable results of this project is that many previously unexplored or forgotten areas were visited and new valuable sites have been identified and will be brought to the attention of the appropriate bodies. The project also provided the opportunity and motivation to study the status of butterflies in the wider countryside and not just within the relative richness of reserves.

This project does not mark the completion of butterfly recording in this area. Rather, it represents the start of a campaign of continuous annual recording to ensure that we have up-to-date information on species distribution and on any threats to their local survival.

	1987	1988	1989	1990	1991	1992	All data 1987-92
Large white	50	66	71	54	71	71	97
Meadow brown	60	59	69	67	68	58	95
Small white	54	58	71	62	73	61	95
Small tortoiseshell	65	56	66	60	63	59	90
Green-veined white	39	45	53	51	62	58	90
Gatekeeper	45	47	55	54	65	51	88
Peacock	47	51	53	50	54	55	81
Speckled wood	53	59	66	53	52	47	80
Orange-tip	41	40	43	46	44	43	74
Holly blue	5	5	27	59	59	27	72
Ringlet	39	39	42	39	40	34	70
Small skipper	34	33	39	37	47	35	68
Brimstone	34	40	42	42	43	40	65
Red admiral	43	38	40	38	32	40	63
Large skipper	40	37	37	33	29	25	58
Common blue	32	28	41	34	37	30	57
Comma	37	29	38	35	39	24	56
Small copper	19	14	35	32	25	14	44
Small heath	25	21	28	26	22	17	39
Marbled white	28	23	22	20	23	17	37
Painted lady	10	43	14	15	16	15	33
Essex skipper	8	7	9	11	19	18	29
Wall brown	8	7	11	15	10	3	21
Purple hairstreak	6	3	5	8	7	6	14
Brown argus	7	5	6	5	5	5	10
Dingy skipper	8	8	4	3	3	3	7
Grizzled skipper	7	4	2	5	4	3	7
Small blue	6	5	6	4	2	3	6
White admiral	7	3	4	2	1	3	6
Dark green fritillary	8	6	4	3	2	1	5
Green hairstreak	5	4	3	3	2	3	5
White-letter hairstreak	3	1	2	2	2	2	4
Chalkhill blue	3	4	4	2	3	3	4
Clouded yellow	0.8	0.2	0.8	0.6	0.3	4.4	3.3
Wood white	2.6	2.2	1.2	0.7	1.6	0.8	2.5
Black hairstreak	6.1	1.3	1.0	0.2	0.3	0.9	2.3
Duke of Burgundy	3.1	3.4	1.3	1.4	1.4	0.7	1.8
Silver washed fritillary	1.3	0.4	1.2	0.7	0.5	0.3	1.4
Grayling	0.8	0.2	0.5	1.0	0.6	1.1	1.3
Purple emperor	0.5	0.4	0.7	0.5	0.7		1.1
Brown hairstreak	1.8	0.7	0.4	0.2	0.1	0.2	0.7
Silver-spotted skipper	0.8	0.4	0.8	0.4	0.3	0.8	0.7
Silver-studded blue	0.3		0.3	0.7	0.3	0.7	0.7
Marsh fritillary	1.3	0.7	0.5	0.2	0.2	0.1	0.5
Adonis blue	0.3	0.4	0.7	0.4	0.5	0.3	0.4
Pearl-bordered Fritillary	0.8	0.4	0.1	0.2	0.2	0.2	0.4
Small Pearl-bordered fritillary	0.5	0.2	0.3	0.1			0.1
Large tortoiseshell	0.3			0.1			0.1
Recorded squares	391	446	765	962	1177	892	1560

Percentage of recorded squares in which each species was seen each year of the survey, arranged in descending order

Representation of data

At the head of each species account a flight season chart is given, and distribution maps show relative numbers seen. The following colour schemes are used.

The local flight season for species recorded locally is shown using a 'calendar strip'. The deepest colour is used to depict periods when the butterflies were seen in every year of the survey (given suitable weather conditions on the day), while a paler shading is used to show when they were seen in some years, but not in others. A few species overwinter as adults, and if disturbed could conceivably be seen throughout the winter months; this is indicated by a blue shading on the calendar strip. An example is shown here to illustrate the key used.

JAN	FEB	MAR	APR	MAY	JUNE	JULY	AUG	SEPT	OCT	NOV	DEC

Distribution maps show all the records for butterflies seen during the atlas survey period (1987 to 1992) over the whole area of the three counties. Although the formal survey ended in 1992, records received for 1993 have also been incorporated. Records for each 2 km square (tetrad) in which that species was recorded are plotted using different symbols to represent the maximum number of individual butterflies seen in that square in any one year. These range from only one individual seen (possibly an accidental sighting) to representation of a well established colony. The key is given in the examples below (see also page 7). This conveys a more realistic impression of the true status of colonies than a simple dot map with a single symbol can show. For some species additional 10 km square maps are used to make comparisons with historical records.

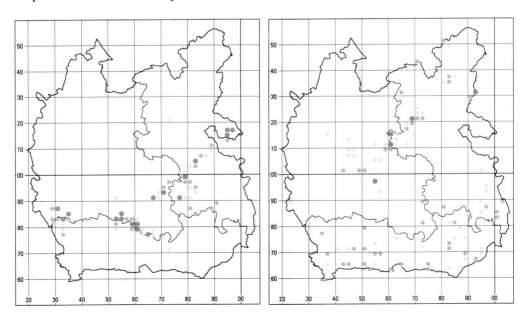

LEFT Chalkhill blue
RIGHT White admiral

Key:
· 1 record
· 2–9 records
● 10+ records

THE SKIPPERS

THE SKIPPERS are a family of small and rather moth-like butterflies. They are, in fact, closer taxonomically to some moth species than they are to the rest of the butterfly families. They have rather squat, hairy bodies similar in length to their wings – in other butterfly species, the wings are much longer than the body. They have broad heads with wide-set eyes and the antennae of some species have hooked tips.

Skippers are named after their very fast and darting flight pattern, low over the ground, which makes them difficult to follow. In the local area, the family includes some of the more common species and one of the rarest and most threatened. They are easily overlooked, because of their fast flight and small size, and are consequently among the least well-known of our butterflies.

The first four species are rather closely related and share characteristics of general form and a distinctive way of holding their forewings swept back and half open at an angle of about 45° above their hindwings, which are held flat, when feeding or basking. This pose is illustrated in some of the species photographs. It is not clear why they do this. This position may give them an advantage in assisting them to make their characteristically fast take-off from a stationary position. Alternatively, they may adopt this pose to pick up more heat from the sun as they cannot extend their forewings forward of the hindwings in the normally recognised butterfly shape.

The eggs of these four species are smooth and quite large for butterflies. Their caterpillars are all grass-feeders but not necessarily on the same grass species. The eggs are laid and the caterpillars conceal themselves within the grass leaf sheath, often feeding from the tip. They are also equipped with a comb-like mechanism used to project droppings some distance away, to avoid leaving tell-tale signs on the ground below.

The last two species are representatives of a larger European group, all of which hold their wings in a more conventional open position. The eggs of these species are spherical with vertical ribs. Their caterpillars are herb-eaters, but share with the other skippers the habit of building a nest of leaves within which they feed.

The skippers are usually single-brooded in this area, although they have different flight seasons, and overwinter as caterpillars.

SMALL SKIPPER *Thymelicus sylvestris*

Flight season	JAN	FEB	MAR	APR	MAY	JUNE	JULY	AUG	SEPT	OCT	NOV	DEC

Micrograph of small skipper eggs laid in the grass leaf sheath

THE SMALL SKIPPER is a widely distributed species of rough grassland. It is distinguished from the large skipper by its smaller size and the plain orange-brown colour of its wings, without patterning. The main photograph shows a male small skipper in a typical basking pose. The male has a thin line of black scent scales on the forewing – this line is absent in the female. This species is easily confused with the Essex skipper, but can be distinguished in the field (see Essex skipper for the key differences).

Small skippers are found in rough grassland in open aspects, including downland and unimproved meadow, in dry, sunny woodland rides and clearings and on embankments, cuttings and roadside verges. Adult males set up small territories and fly up aggressively to challenge other insects approaching. They spend long periods basking in sunshine and nectaring on many flowers, including brambles, thistles and knapweeds. They hold their wings in a typical half-open pose, as shown in the photograph.

In the local area, adults fly between mid- or late June to late August in a single brood. The emergence time of the species varies by as much as two weeks from year to year, depending on weather conditions. Although the flying season extends over eight weeks, individual adult insects may only survive for about five days.

The female chooses soft grasses, such as Yorkshire-fog, for egg laying. She lands on the grass head and then crawls backwards down the stem to lay up to eight eggs at a time within the grass leaf sheath. The eggs are pale yellow and shiny, resembling miniature peeled potatoes. The caterpillars emerge 3–4 weeks later, eat part of their egg shells and then spin

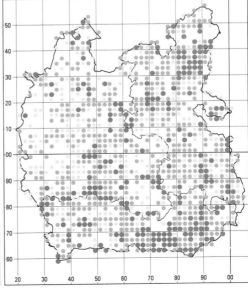

a cocoon within the grass sheath for hibernation. They emerge the following spring to begin feeding from within tubes formed from grass blades. The pupa is formed within a tent of leaves and silk spun near to the ground.

Within this area, the species is widely distributed and common wherever suitable habitat is found. The main threats to the species are over-frequent grass-cutting, 'improvement' of grassland and meadow for intensive agriculture and loss of habitat to development.

ESSEX SKIPPER *Thymelicus lineola*

JAN	FEB	MAR	APR	MAY	JUNE	JULY	AUG	SEPT	OCT	NOV	DEC

Flight season

Essex skipper showing black tips on antennae

ESSEX SKIPPER adults are very similar in appearance to those of the small skipper, with a tendency to be slightly smaller. The main photograph shows a male in typical basking pose, with wings held half-open.

There are two key features that allow Essex skippers to be distinguished from small skippers in the field. One is that the lines of black scent scales in the middle of the upper forewings of the male adult Essex skipper are parallel to the outer edge of the wing, whereas in the small skipper the line is slightly off parallel. The easier feature to notice is that the undersides of the tips of the antennae of the Essex skipper are a dense black, often described as if the tips had been 'dipped in Indian ink' (see photograph taken head-on). Those of the small skipper are dark brown on the upperside of the tip and light on the underside. To see this in the field, you have to look the butterfly square on in the face. This generally requires

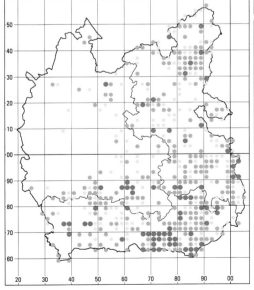

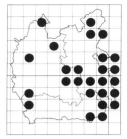

Essex skipper records,
1975–1984

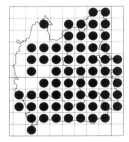

Essex skipper records,
1987–1992

getting down in the undergrowth slowly without disturbing it by sudden movement – hence the odd postures sometimes adopted by keen butterfly-watchers!

Essex skippers are found in rough grassland habitats with medium-length grasses, including roadside and track verges, embankments and cuttings, often sharing habitats with small skippers. Detailed habitat requirements are not well understood for the Essex skipper and it may dominate small skippers at particular sites for no obvious reason.

The butterfly makes short rapid darting flights, the male defending a small territory and rising to challenge approaching insects. It is often found basking in sunlight or nectaring with its forewings held in a half-raised position, like the small and large skippers. This wing position may aid the rapid take-off which is a feature of these species. For feeding it favours bramble flowers, knapweeds and thistles.

The local flight season is from early or mid-July through to mid- or late August. The timing depends on weather conditions earlier in the year and can vary by up to two weeks between seasons. Typically the flight season is one to two weeks later than that of the small skipper. Eggs are laid, generally in small numbers, within the leaf sheath of soft grasses, such as cock's-foot. The female lands on the grass stem and crawls down, working the tip of her abdomen into the grass sheath and spending several seconds laying eggs inside. The caterpillars do not hatch until the following spring, in contrast to those of the small skipper which emerge shortly after the eggs are laid. This difference probably explains their later emergence as adults. They then eat from within a tube formed by sticking the edges of a grass blade together and are therefore seldom seem.

The Essex skipper, as its name would suggest, was historically confined to the south-east of England. It has however been spreading gradually westwards. Within this local area, although the distribution is predominantly in the eastern half of the region, the butterfly is now well-established in all three counties. Within the last year of the survey (1992) the species was found for the first time in many more locations in mid- and south Oxfordshire, including several parts of the Ridgeway and associated footpaths. The *Atlas of Oxfordshire Butterflies* (Knight and Campbell 1982) noted only six sites in Oxfordshire and kept them confidential due to the apparent rarity of the butterfly at that time. Now there are over six times this number, and it has also been found in Wiltshire and Warwickshire.

The map on the previous page shows the current distribution of the species. The extent of recent colonisation is indicated by the additional maps of 10 km square records for 1975–1984 and 1987–1992, clearly showing the westward diffusion. It is likely that there are many more sites yet to be found in mid- and perhaps north Oxfordshire.

It has been suggested that the move westwards is facilitated by roadside verges, which provide suitable conditions for the butterfly, and that motorway verges, in particular, provide a good continuity of habitat to ease rapid movement. Although this is a tempting theory, railways have been in existence for a long time and long-distance footpaths for a lot longer – why did it not move before? Perhaps the explanation also involves a gradual climate change encouraging the move westwards. There is also a theory that eggs are accidentally transported in hay lorries, now moving comparatively long distances.

The Essex skipper is, within its range, a widespread species where there is suitable habitat. Locally, it is likely to be lost where grass verges are cut too frequently or where scrub invasion blocks out direct sunlight from the ground vegetation.

SILVER-SPOTTED SKIPPER *Hesperia comma*

JAN	FEB	MAR	APR	MAY	JUNE	JULY	AUG	SEPT	OCT	NOV	DEC	Flight season

SILVER-SPOTTED SKIPPERS take their name from the pattern of silver-white spots on the undersides of their wings, visible in the photograph of an adult basking on the bare chalky soil of its preferred habitat. The upperside of the wings runs from a rich dark brown to a lighter orange-brown, with orange spots corresponding to the silver spots on the underside. The female is similar to the male, but lacks the black bar of scent scales along the centre of the forewing.

The counties of Berkshire, Buckinghamshire and Oxfordshire are at the northern limit of the range of the silver-spotted skipper. The right habitat is crucial to the survival of this species at the few local sites on which it is still found. These are sites on chalk grassland, where the turf length is very short, often grazed by rabbits, with patches of bare soil interspersed amongst the turf, often due to land slip, rabbit digging or hoof damage. These patches of soil are vital, allowing the bare ground to be baked by the sun, raising the temperature near to the soil by as much as 20°C above shade temperature. This high temperature microclimate provides the necessary conditions for the species to complete its life-cycle within the year. If the conditions change, for example by a reduction in

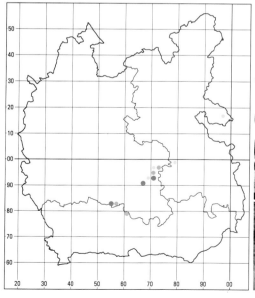

Close-up of silver-spotted
skipper egg on grass stem

grazing, and longer vegetation shades the ground, the surface temperature will drop. This means that completion of the life-cycle within the year becomes impossible and the species will become extinct from that site.

The butterfly spends a great deal of time basking in sunlight and nectaring, often from the dwarf thistles typical of its habitat. The wings are held partly open, as with the previous two species of skipper. The silver-spotted skipper has a very quick take-off and a fast, buzzing, darting flight that makes it very hard to follow by eye. The forewings are noticeably curved in shape, probably increasing their flight efficiency and enhancing their speed.

Adult butterflies fly in a single brood from late July to mid-September and are the latest of the skippers to appear in the year. White eggs, shaped like Christmas puddings, are laid singly in small clumps of the very fine sheep's-fescue grass, usually on the edge of a small patch of bare stony soil. The caterpillar hatches the following spring and makes a nest from silk and grass blades, which it uses as a base for feeding. Being dark green, it is difficult to find. It has an interesting way of protecting itself from being eaten by grazing animals. If it detects warm breath, it goes straight down to soil level, until the hazard has passed. It pupates within a cocoon formed near to the ground amongst grass stems.

In this area, the silver-spotted skipper is found only on very short chalk grassland on the Downs and Chilterns. As a result of its specialist habitat requirements and the loss of suitable sites, this species is now recorded at only 11 sites in the three counties. Silver-spotted skippers were once recorded at sites as far north as Yorkshire, but today the butterfly is restricted to chalk grasslands of southern central England. These sites also support chalkhill blues, which have similar habitat requirements.

In the few locations where they still occur, silver-spotted skipper colonies can be large. It is seldom found very far from suitable habitat. The main threat to the species is the loss of suitable microclimate conditions in its habitat, for example due to changes in grazing (perhaps because of myxomatosis in rabbits) or scrub invasion. If the species is lost from a particular site, natural re-colonisation is very unlikely, because colonies are now too isolated. Monitoring and management of those remaining sites is therefore very important.

LARGE SKIPPER *Ochlodes venata*

Flight season	JAN	FEB	MAR	APR	MAY	JUNE	JULY	AUG	SEPT	OCT	NOV	DEC

THE LARGE SKIPPER is significantly larger than the small and Essex skipper. The adult varies in colour, with deep brown through to orange-brown wings patterned with lighter spots. The contrast of the spots is variable, in some specimens showing as very clearly chequered. In the early eighteenth century, this species was called the 'Checkered Hog' by Petiver, referring both to the pattern and to its squat shape. The male has a black band of scent scales running across the forewing.

Like the small skipper, this species is common and found in a wide variety of rough grassland locations, in open areas and within woodlands where there are sunny rides and clearings. In most places both large and small skippers are found together, flying with a very similar fast buzzing flight close to the ground.

The wings are held in a half open position when basking or nectaring, ready for a fast take-off. In cool weather, the adult turns to a position square-on to the sun so as to pick up the maximum heat. The male often basks on the leaf of a large plant, such as on bracken or on leaves of meadowsweet, using it as a vantage point for defending its territory.

Underside of the large skipper

Locally, the flying season lasts from early June to mid-August, but this can vary by as much as two weeks from year to year. The large skipper usually emerges about two weeks earlier than the small skipper and it is also single-brooded. Eggs are laid singly on the undersides of the blades of its foodplant, which is normally cock's-foot grass. The caterpillar feeds within a grass tube, eating from the top end. It hibernates when part-grown and emerges again the following spring to resume feeding. It forms a pupa low down in a nest spun with silk and leaves within a grass clump, from which it emerges about three weeks later.

Large skippers are found all over the local area and are amongst the most frequently recorded skippers. As well as the larger open grassland areas such as meadows, they can colonise relatively small habitats, including roadside verges, undisturbed field margins and set-aside corners. Neither the small nor the large skipper is found on monoculture 'improved' grassland, where the foodplant is absent. The relative adaptability of the large skipper would seem to protect this species from extinction, but careless mowing or cultivation on a wide scale poses a real threat.

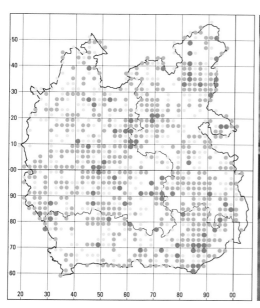

DINGY SKIPPER *Erynnis tages*

Flight season	JAN	FEB	MAR	APR	MAY	JUNE	JULY	AUG	SEPT	OCT	NOV	DEC

THE DINGY SKIPPER is well-named. From a distance it is drab and unattractive, and is easily mistaken for a moth, or even more likely, overlooked completely. It has not compromised in having effective camouflage. A closer look is rewarding, however, as it has modest but intricate patterning on the wings. The photograph shows it in a typical basking pose, when it almost always has its wings fully open. Specimens appear even more dingy and drab when they become worn.

The male and female are very similar and difficult to distinguish in the field. The female tends to be slightly larger with slightly bolder colouring than the male.

It is a species of chalk and limestone grassland, although it is also found on other grassy sites where its foodplants grow. It prefers open but sheltered habitats, usually south-facing, with medium-short grass and a warm microclimate near the soil. Some woodland colonies are also known, where there are open, sunny rides.

Like the other skippers, the dingy skipper has a fast erratic flight close to the ground, which, combined with its drab colour, makes it very difficult to watch. This species is mainly single-brooded, flying from early May to late June. At some warm sites, a second brood occurs, flying in mid-August.

Eggs are laid singly on common bird's-foot-trefoil, mainly on the youngest growth. In chalk habitats it may also use horseshoe vetch. The eggs are shaped like a rounded jelly-mould, with vertical ribs. They are green when laid, but turn orange after a few days. The caterpillar emerges and constructs a little tent by spinning silk around a few leaves in

24

which it lives and eats, moving on to make larger tents as it grows. The fully grown caterpillar, grey-green with a shiny black head, forms a last tent for hibernation. It turns into a pupa the following spring.

The distribution of this species matches that of the grizzled skipper quite closely with many local sites supporting both species. The most obvious correlation is with the grassland of the Downs and Chilterns, but there are several other colonies elsewhere on limestone grassland and in woodland.

The dingy skipper depends on having suitable habitat with a good supply of foodplants and open, sunny flying and basking positions. Overwhelming scrub cover or over-rank grass growth leads to local extinction.

GRIZZLED SKIPPER *Pyrgus malvae*

JAN	FEB	MAR	APR	MAY	JUNE	JULY	AUG	SEPT	OCT	NOV	DEC

Flight season

Grizzled skipper underside

THE GRIZZLED SKIPPER is often overlooked. It is a small butterfly with deep brown and cream chequered wings that provide excellent camouflage in the dry grassy areas it prefers, and locating it requires persistence and a good eye. As a result, it almost certainly occurs on more sites than its distribution map would imply. The undersides are a pale off-white colour with green-brown chequered markings and are seen only when it is roosting in cool overcast conditions.

There are only subtle visual differences between male and female and, in practice, they are difficult to distinguish in the field.

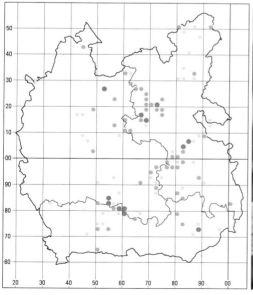

Grizzled skippers inhabit dry grassy areas with short vegetation, where the foodplants, wild strawberry or related plants, including cinquefoil and tormentil, are found. The butterfly prefers relatively sheltered and hot locations, such as chalk or limestone areas with partial scrub cover, dry woodland rides and clearings. It can often be found on the dry stony bed of disused railway cuttings, where there is a good variety of herb-rich vegetation.

The flight is very fast and blurred, so that the butterflies are very difficult to follow. When they bask or nectar, they keep their wings fully open and flat, although they are very difficult to approach for close examination and will fly off rapidly if they detect even a small movement.

The adults fly during May and June – the start and finish of the flying season varies from year to year, but it is regarded as a spring butterfly. The species is normally single-brooded. Very rarely, in a very hot year, there may be a partial second brood, flying in August.

Eggs are laid singly on the foodplant. They are similar in form to those of the dingy skipper, but are almost white in colour. The newly emerged caterpillar forms a thin shelter of silk on a leaf and feeds from the areas around its edges. In later stages, it folds the edges of a leaf together with silk to make a shelter. It forms a silk nest in vegetation near the ground, in which it pupates and then goes into hibernation.

This species is found on many sites in the area, within isolated but often strong colonies in appropriate short dry grassland conditions. As the map shows, these are more common on the chalk grasslands of the Downs and Chilterns and on the limestones of north Oxfordshire and north Buckinghamshire. There are several colonies on disused railway lines in north Buckinghamshire and it is also found on dry rides in the woodlands of mid-Buckinghamshire and mid-Oxfordshire.

As a potentially overlooked species, some of its sites may be threatened without our realising. The main threats are from scrubbing-over of grassland sites and from over-development of woodlands, for example for shooting, where use of large machinery can severely damage the soil structure and established vegetation.

THE WHITES
AND YELLOWS

THE WHITES or, more accurately, the whites and yellows, have a number of features in common. As their common names suggest, most of these species tend to be mainly white or yellow in appearance. Their eggs are long, thin and bottle-shaped, with vertical ribs. The caterpillars are mainly green in colour and have no protective spines. In some species, the colour is supplemented by longitudinal markings to aid concealment. Apart from the brimstone, they feed on herbs and overwinter as pupae. Five of the species are widespread (two of these are well-known but unwelcome garden pests), one species is an unusual immigrant to this local area and one is very localised and significantly threatened by loss of suitable habitat.

One former resident species of this family, the black-veined white, is long extinct in this country – its caterpillars eat leaves of blackthorn and hawthorn, but also fruit trees and therefore it was once a pest of orchards, particularly in Kent. It disappeared from its last strongholds in south-east England in the 1920s, for reasons that are not understood. In its former breeding sites in Britain and in those parts of continental Europe where it still occurs, numbers are known to fluctuate strongly from year to year for no apparent reason. It is only rarely seen in Britain now.

The caterpillars that feed on plants of the cabbage family have evolved to digest and store the toxic ingredients of the mustard oils from their foodplants, making them poisonous and very distasteful to predators. When disturbed they can emit a strong and unpleasant smell. The waste products are used to make the white and yellow pigments in the wings of the adults. The black markings on several species tend to be lighter in the spring broods and darker in the summer broods.

The white species (large, small and green-veined) are not easy to distinguish in flight, and positive identification usually has to wait until they settle. They are difficult to approach and fly up nervously at the slightest disturbance, behaviour probably developed for defence as the bold white colouring does not provide convenient camouflage, although small whites are sometimes concealed very effectively amongst the white leaves of variegated dogwood in the garden.

WOOD WHITE *Leptidea sinapis*

Flight season	JAN	FEB	MAR	APR	MAY	JUNE	JULY	AUG	SEPT	OCT	NOV	DEC

Mating wood whites on a bird's-foot-trefoil flower – the female is on the right

THE FRAIL fluttering flight of the wood white, the smallest of the British white butterflies, is characteristic and allows it to be identified with reasonable confidence from a distance. But although the flight appears frail, it is deceptive – they will fly continuously for tens of minutes, frustrating attempts to observe them closely.

The forewings have a rounded shape differing from the more angular form of the other whites, and the butterfly has a much longer and thinner body. Across the underside of the hindwings there is a light patterning of grey or grey-yellow scales, broadly following the lines of the wing veins. On the outer tips of the uppersides of the forewings there is a circular dark grey patch, which can be glimpsed in flight or seen in silhouette. The female is slightly larger than the male and has slightly more rounded wing tips.

Wood whites have a strong preference for shady woodland habitats, where they may be found fluttering slowly but methodically along ride edges, never straying very far from ground level. This slow controlled flight is suited to these enclosed habitats. The typical damp woodlands where the wood white is found in strong colonies are on the heavy clay soils of north Buckinghamshire and mid-Oxfordshire, as shown on the distribution map, with some small colonies elsewhere. It is very colonial and seldom wanders out of its local woodland habitat. In its best sites, many tens of individuals can be counted and it may be the commonest white butterfly in favoured locations. Adults are fond of nectaring from woodland flowers, especially bugle, vetches and trefoils.

28

Wood whites are predominantly single-brooded, peaking in June, although a small second brood may occur in warm summers in late July or mid-August. They have a curious courting ritual, illustrated by Thomas and Lewington (in *The Butterflies of Britain and Ireland*, 1991), during which the male waves his uncoiled proboscis and antennae to and fro and the female responds by bending her abdomen towards the male. The eggs, pale green-white with the characteristic bottle shape, are laid singly on young leaves of vetches – chiefly meadow vetchling, bitter-vetch and tufted vetch – in rather shaded locations, often along ride edges. The caterpillars are green with a yellow stripe along each side and eat the young leaves of the foodplant. Hibernation occurs as a pupa.

Numbers can vary quite dramatically from one year to the next, but since this variation occurs on sites with apparently stable habitats, it is almost certainly due to changes in seasonal weather patterns or to changes in levels of attack by tiny parasitic wasps of the *Trichogramma* genus, to which wood white eggs are vulnerable.

Many of the wood white's former sites have been lost, due to extremes of dereliction or clearance of woodland. Where wood whites do occur, in both deciduous, mixed and coniferous woodland, stable habitats are provided by sheltered woodland rides and small clearings. Overgrown rides, however, can become too heavily shaded for both the butterfly and its foodplants, and numbers will dwindle. On the other hand, clear felling of woodland on a large scale can easily obliterate suitable habitat, with total loss resulting. Wood white habitat can be maintained by traditional coppice management in which the shrubby regrowth stage provides the most suitable conditions.

CLOUDED YELLOW *Colias croceus*

JAN	FEB	MAR	APR	MAY	JUNE	JULY	AUG	SEPT	OCT	NOV	DEC	Flight season

CLOUDED YELLOWS are unusual but unmistakable immigrants to this area. In flight, they show off their vivid orange-yellow uppersides, with bold black outer margins on the wings. The male has fully black margins; the female has yellow spots within the margins on the upperside. When settled or nectaring they keeps their wings closed, showing yellow undersides with a characteristic red-ringed figure-of-eight mark in the centre. There is a pale variety of the female, known as *helice*, where the orange-yellow coloration is replaced by white-grey, but it is rarely seen in the three counties.

The clouded yellow is a resident of southern Europe and north Africa. However, it spreads north vigorously and in England is seen regularly along the south coast, but is only occasionally found further inland. In some years, however, there is a population explosion in southern Europe and a large migration results, assisted by suitable prevailing winds. This was the case in 1983, when the species was sighted in many local areas. Large numbers could be seen in fields of lucerne, one of its foodplants, the flowers of which clouded yellows find particularly attractive.

Between 1987 and 1991 there were only a few scattered sightings of clouded yellows in this area. The next year, 1992, turned out to be a very interesting one for this species in Britain and a spectacular one in Scotland, where it had previously been recorded in the south, but very rarely further north. In May, a large influx crossed western Ireland and penetrated to north-west Scotland. Large numbers were seen in many areas as the butterfly spread and bred further inland. By summer, clouded yellows were present in very large numbers throughout Scotland and in west Wales. In the local area, there were about 40 sightings scattered across the three counties. In some places two or three butterflies were seen flying together. The distribution map shows all records over the atlas period, but these are dominated by the 1992 sightings.

Early arrivals mate and lay eggs singly, mainly on clover, lucerne and trefoils. The eggs are white when newly laid, but turn pink-orange. The caterpillars are a dull grey-green, with a yellow stripe streaked with red along each side. They pupate after about a month of vigorous feeding. The resulting population of adults emerging 8–10 weeks later can be significantly larger than the original influx, but neither they nor their caterpillars or pupae can survive our cold, damp winters and although some will migrate back to the south, many simply die.

It may well be many years before there is another large clouded yellow influx on the scale of 1983 or of 1992. These mass invasions occur very erratically and unpredictably and the factors driving them are not understood. If large-scale loss of habitat occurs in southern Europe in the future, and continental populations are reduced, then even the occasional clouded yellow invasions into this country may be threatened. If continental populations continue to thrive, however, we should still see this colourful butterfly from time to time.

BRIMSTONE *Gonepteryx rhamni*

JAN	FEB	MAR	APR	MAY	JUNE	JULY	AUG	SEPT	OCT	NOV	DEC

Flight season

Male (yellow) and female (pale) brimstones nectaring

THE BRIMSTONE has one of the longest adult life-spans of any of our butterflies and is often the first species seen in the year. The male has bright sulphur-yellow uppersides, making it very easy to identify in flight, even from a distance. Indeed, there is a theory (one of several) that the name 'butterfly' is based on this species – the butter-coloured fly.

The female has a pale green colour, lacking the strong yellow pigment of the male, and can easily be mistaken for another white species. Both male and female have wine-red heads and antennae, easily seen when they are spotted nectaring. The antennae are bent forward at the tips, rather like hockey sticks. There is a small orange spot above the centre of each wing, on the upper side, with a corresponding darker red spot on the underside. The other characteristic of this species is the very angular shape of the wing tips and the strongly developed veins on the wings. These are exploited as excellent camouflage when the butterfly is roosting or hibernating upside down under foliage, as shown in the photograph below.

When nectaring, brimstones are particularly attracted to large red or purple flowers, including knapweeds, thistles and teasels in the wild and buddleia, sweet pea and runner bean flowers in the garden. It exploits its unusually long proboscis to reach into the deep nectaries of these large flowers, which few other butterflies can reach. The long life of the adult (up to 11 months), far-ranging flight and the demands of hibernation require large fat stocks built up by long periods of nectaring.

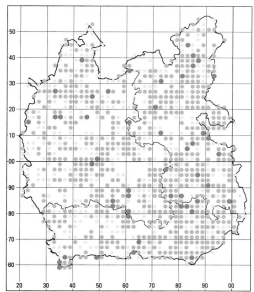

Adults emerge from the pupa in mid-summer and will fly late into autumn and during the winter on unusually mild and sunny days, returning to roost when the sun drops low. They are seen with increasing frequency through spring until they disappear after mating and egg-laying.

Eggs are laid singly in spring on the unfurling young leaf shoots of buckthorn (on calcareous soils) or alder buckthorn (on damp acid soils), the only foodplants of brimstone caterpillars. It is generally thought that the national distribution of this species is limited mainly by the distribution of its foodplants. The two distributions match very closely. Brimstones are strong wanderers and females will seek out even individual isolated shrubs. The caterpillar is a dull green colour with diffuse white lines along each side and is well camouflaged against the dull green leaves of the foodplant; the pupa also mimics a leaf.

As shown by the distribution map, this is a common and widespread species. Where there are gaps, they probably reflect lack of recording rather than absence, as the foodplants are relatively common. It is found in a wide variety of habitats, including open woodland, hedgerows, grassland and gardens, where it is generally seen in ones or twos. On some downland sites, where there is a good variety of mixed scrub/woodland and grassland, it can be quite numerous. Numbers do not vary very strongly from year to year, and the relative abundance of buckthorn in the three counties maintains its status.

LARGE WHITE *Pieris brassicae*

Flight season	JAN	FEB	MAR	APR	MAY	JUNE	JULY	AUG	SEPT	OCT	NOV	DEC

THE LARGE WHITE is perhaps the least popular garden butterfly due to its caterpillars' taste for cabbage and related plants (hence the name 'cabbage white' used for both the large and the small white). The black, yellow and green caterpillars of this species feed in gangs on *Brassica* plants in the garden and will strip them completely of their foliage if left unchecked. They may also attack the flower bed, as they have a particular liking for nasturtiums and have also been found feeding on leaves of honesty and dame's-violet. They are not just a species of the garden, however, and are found throughout the countryside where they use many wild plants of the cabbage family.

The adult butterfly is attractive, with its large white wings, tipped with bold black markings and spots. The undersides of the hindwings have a rather yellow tinge which can vary in strength.

Large whites are found in a very wide variety of habitats, including woodland, grassland, hedgerows, farmland and urban areas, and were recorded in most squares. They have a strong fluttering flight and can fly fast over long distances. In woodland, they nectar from various flowers, including bluebells, thistles and knapweeds. In the garden, the large white is a frequently-observed visitor to the buddleia bush.

There are two broods of the large white each year. In this country, it overwinters as a pupa. The adult butterflies which emerge in spring are often boosted by immigrant adults

from the continent. This generation lays eggs in May or June, producing a second generation in late summer, whose caterpillars pupate in late autumn. In domestic environments, caterpillars often scale house and shed walls, dispersing to pupate under eaves and soffits. In a plentiful year many tens of pupae may be found around a typical house.

The eggs, yellow and bottle-shaped, are laid in fairly large batches in neat hexagonal arrays on the undersides of its foodplant leaves; the inset photograph shows the start of a cycle familiar to the gardener. The caterpillars hatch together after a week or two and begin their systematic and ugly destruction of the plant. As they feed, they accumulate poisonous mustard oils from the plant, which makes them unpalatable to predators. Their warning coloration advertises this fact and they are able to reinforce this by emitting a pungent smell when disturbed.

Array of large white eggs on a cabbage leaf

The large white is often heavily parasitised by a small *Apanteles* wasp, which lays its eggs in the caterpillar's body. The wasp larvae slowly consume the body fat of the caterpillar, but do not kill it until it is ready to pupate, at which point the wasp larvae burrow out of its body and form a mass of tiny yellow furry cocoons on the outside. The rate of attack is very high and over 90% of caterpillars may be affected, acting as a strong natural control on population growth.

Occasionally, the populations can grow to swarm proportions. In this area, along with other regions, 1992 was notable for the very large numbers of large whites in the late summer brood. There was a large immigrant influx in early summer, leading to a very much larger second brood. This species could be counted in hundreds over fields of rape and on small set-aside areas where thistles and knapweeds attracted them. It is interesting, however, that the 1993 early summer population of this species was very low indeed –

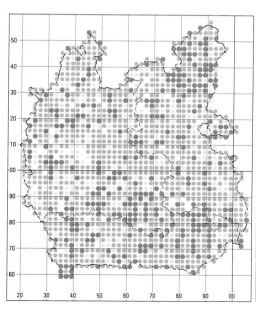

possibly due to parasite attack on an equally large scale combined with a shortage of immigrants due to poor weather conditions.

Large whites do not seem to occur in such large numbers in the wilder parts of the countryside. These large numbers are much more strongly associated with cultivated areas (including gardens), where the large-scale intensive growing of suitable plants encourages them to breed to pest levels. As such, they have probably benefited more from widespread development of the countryside than most species.

For the keen vegetable gardener who also enjoys butterflies, the 'cabbage whites' pose a dilemma: to spray or not to spray. The indiscriminate use of insecticides will kill the parasite predator as well as the target species, and the natural balance is upset. It is better to aim for a specific control. Covering *Brassica* patches with fine netting is one approach – but it has to be entomological rather than fishing net mesh, since they sail happily through the latter. Washing caterpillars off the plants with a hose buys a few days at least, but the caterpillars do return. The patient gardener will pore over the leaves, squashing any eggs and caterpillars found, but that is slow and laborious. Others just give up growing brassicas!

SMALL WHITE *Pieris rapae*

Flight season	JAN	FEB	MAR	APR	MAY	JUNE	JULY	AUG	SEPT	OCT	NOV	DEC

THE SMALL WHITE is perhaps less noticeable than the large white, but is almost equally destructive in the garden. The butterfly is mostly white; the forewings are tipped with black and have two black spots, and there is one black spot on each hindwing.

The undersides of the hindwings are a pale yellowish white. It is distinctly smaller than the large white and does not have quite such a loosely fluttering appearance. In the flower garden, small whites seem to prefer lavender for nectaring, whereas the large white is more often seen on buddleia.

Small whites are found in a wide variety of habitats in the countryside, including woodland rides, hedgerows and open grassland, as well as in the garden. They congregate in large numbers over fields of flowering rape, which they use as a nectar source and probably also as a foodplant for their caterpillars. They have a strong but fluttering flight, and when nectaring will move quickly from one flower to another. On lavender, they will spend only 2–3 seconds on each flower head. They are difficult to approach and rise very quickly if disturbed.

Small white egg on a cabbage leaf

There are two broods of the small white each year, with the largest numbers flying between late March and May and again from July to September, although the prolonged flight period of each brood means that they almost overlap in mid-summer.

Unlike the large white, this species lays its pale green eggs singly on the undersides of its foodplants, but it prefers the same brassicas in the garden. The eggs hatch within a week or two and the caterpillars are solitary, generally preferring to feed on the interior of the plant. This means that they can appear inside cauliflowers in the kitchen – hopefully at the cleaning stage rather than at the table! They rely more on camouflage than on the visual warning deployed by large white caterpillars and their pale green colour matches the leaves of cabbages well. The small yellow spots along each side distinguish the small white caterpillar from that of the green-veined white. They move away from the cabbage patch to pupate, often on fences or walls, or on shrub growth.

Small whites are widely distributed and very common butterflies which, as the map shows, can be seen in virtually every habitat in the area. The abundance of this species can vary quite significantly from brood to brood, but it can always be found. Like large whites, they have almost certainly increased greatly in numbers with agricultural and garden development providing a greater availability of foodplants.

GREEN-VEINED WHITE *Pieris napi*

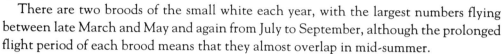

JAN	FEB	MAR	APR	MAY	JUNE	JULY	AUG	SEPT	OCT	NOV	DEC

Flight season

THE MAIN FEATURE that distinguishes the green-veined white from the otherwise very similar small white is the pattern of dark scales along the veins of the wings, which can be seen relatively easily on the undersides of the hindwings. These can vary in strength from a pale grey to a strong dark grey. This dark veining appears also on the uppersides of the wings, but varies between individuals from very light grey to quite pronounced black. The summer brood tends to be more strongly marked than the spring brood. The butterfly flies quite energetically and, like the other whites, is not easy to

35

approach for a close examination, so that clear identification can be tricky without experience and patience.

It is quite common, when watching a male green-veined white courting a female, to see the female settling on a leaf with her wings open, and her abdomen raised. Contrary to appearance, this is a sign of rejection of the male's advances, normally because she has mated already.

Green-veined whites are found in a wide variety of habitats, including woodland rides, grassland, farmland and hedgerows, often along with small whites.

The green-veined white is double-brooded and flies over the same period as the small white. Unlike its similar relatives, the green-veined white selects wild plants of the cabbage family for egg-laying. Often, it will choose the leaves of garlic mustard and will also lay on related plants such as hedge mustard and cuckooflower. Although it often visits the garden, it is not interested in the *Brassica* patch and is not a pest. In general, a typical garden will have more small whites visiting than green-veined whites. In the open countryside, numbers are almost equal, with perhaps more green-veined whites, especially in damp, cooler habitats.

Eggs are laid singly on the undersides of leaves. The caterpillar is pale green and lacks the yellow markings found along the sides of small white caterpillars. The pupa is similar to that of the small white. Hibernation occurs during the pupal stage following the second brood.

The butterfly is widely distributed and very common, occurring in almost every habitat. Where there are a few gaps on the distribution map, it is more probably due to less experienced recorders confusing them for small whites, than because of their absence.

ORANGE-TIP *Anthocharis cardamines*

JAN	FEB	MAR	APR	MAY	JUNE	JULY	AUG	SEPT	OCT	NOV	DEC

Flight season

THE MALE ORANGE-TIP is an easy butterfly to identify, even in flight, due to the prominent orange tips of the uppersides of the forewings. The female, however, completely lacks any orange marking, but can be distinguished from other whites by the dappled scale pattern on the underside of the hindwings, which is present in both sexes. This dappling has a greenish appearance, an optical illusion resulting from a mixture of yellow and black scales, which forms a perfect camouflage when roosting amongst vegetation, especially cow parsley or garlic mustard flowers.

Orange-tips are seen in many different habitats, including open flowery meadows, sunny woodland rides and along paths, hedgerows and roadsides where it flies vigorously. It is a fairly frequent visitor to the garden where it may stop to nectar on early flowers. It flies quite extensively and seems to spread to find its foodplants wherever they occur in sunlit spots.

The orange-tip's flight period lasts from spring to early summer. They have been seen as early as mid-March when there is prolonged mild weather early in the year and occasionally as late as July.

Eggs are laid singly on the flower stems of various wild plants of the cabbage family. In damp unimproved meadows, cuckooflower is chosen. Along roadside verges and hedgerows, the vigorous flowers of garlic mustard are commonly used and sometimes the straggly growths of hedge mustard as well. Occasionally, eggs are laid on honesty in the garden, if there is no garlic mustard available. The eggs are a pale greenish-white when newly laid,

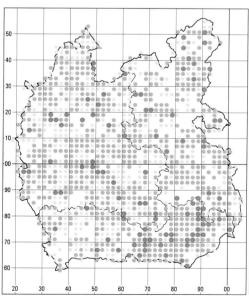

37

but turn a characteristic orange colour within a matter of hours. They are amongst the easiest butterfly eggs to find and can be located simply by inspecting the seed pods and flower stems near the tops of the foodplants in late spring. The small but elongated bottle-shaped orange eggs are attached end-on to the stem, usually just below a flower head or bud. They hatch about a week to ten days after they are laid.

Orange-tip caterpillar feeding on garlic mustard

The newly-emerged caterpillar first eats most of the egg shell, before moving on to feed on the developing seed pods of the plant, which are rich in protein and provide for rapid development. The caterpillars are cannibalistic and will eat other orange-tip eggs – if one caterpillar encounters another, the larger eats the smaller. This is presumably a defence mechanism against the dangers of overfeeding on a single isolated plant, ensuring that there is enough food for at least one caterpillar to survive. The early stage of the caterpillar is a dull grey-brown colour. At a mid-stage of its development, the caterpillar produces beads of sweet liquid at the ends of the hairs on its body which attract ants. It is not known clearly what benefit the caterpillars gain from this interaction. The ants may provide some protection for the caterpillar from attack by other insects such as wasps. This association with ants occurs much more commonly in the lycaenid butterflies, especially the blues. At later stages in its growth, the caterpillar is green, with a diffuse white line along each side. It lies along the seed pod and can be difficult to spot without practice.

In mid-summer, the caterpillar pupates low in the vegetation and overwinters in that stage. The pupa is long, curved and pointed. It attaches itself to a stem at its lower end and is suspended out at an angle, supported by a strand of silk spun around its body. In this position it effectively imitates a folded leaf.

Over the last decade, the orange-tip has become an increasingly common species and there are now few places in the local area where it cannot be seen. Although its traditional unimproved damp meadow habitats, with abundant cuckooflower, are becoming much more scarce, the flushes of garlic mustard and nectar flowers on country roadside verges left uncut and unsprayed by money-saving local authorities provide ample opportunities for this species and may have led to the expansion in numbers in recent years.

HAIRSTREAKS, COPPERS AND BLUES

THE LYCAENIDAE family is one of the largest and most widely ranging, comprising about a third of the world's 20,000 butterfly species. This family includes the hairstreaks, the coppers and the blues. Lycaenids are mostly small but striking butterflies, often with strongly territorial habits. Many species in this family have characteristic black and white striped antennae and legs. In Berkshire, Buckinghamshire and Oxfordshire the family includes some common and very widespread species, and some of the most localised and endangered of our butterflies.

The caterpillars of all the lycaenids have a similar slug-like shape, but differ considerably between species in their colouring. A number of species have an association with ants at the caterpillar or pupa stage. This has been well established for the large blue, but there is considerable evidence for significant, but perhaps less critical, associations in other species.

THE HAIRSTREAKS. The hairstreaks are shy and retiring species which are small and difficult to observe. They are species of scrub and tree canopy rather than open habitats. They have a characteristic fast and erratic flight, which is a help in recognising them once you become familiar with it, but which makes them difficult to follow.

The name of this group comes from the thin markings or 'streaks' across the hindwings found on all these species. They also all have short tails on the lower edge of the hindwings.

Hairstreaks are localised species which do not readily disperse and tend to be very selective in their habitat requirements, for reasons that are not well understood. There are only a few sites locally where all five species can be found.

THE COPPERS. Only one species from this group, the small copper, is found in this area. The only other UK species, the large copper, finally became extinct in the 1800s after the widespread loss of its large wetland habitats in England due to land drainage. Another close sub-species was introduced into Woodwalton Fen nature reserve in Cambridgeshire in the 1920s, but its viability there is poor, and releases from captive-bred stock have to be made periodically to maintain the population.

THE BLUES. Seven of our remaining eight British blues, including the brown argus, are found in this area. The large blue, not included in this number, became extinct in Britain when its last known colony died out in 1979, although it is now the subject of a re-introduction programme. It was formerly known to occur in the Cotswolds and in the past was probably also found on the Downs.

Blues are most numerous on dry chalk and limestone grasslands. Two species are at the northern limit of their European range in this area and therefore occur only under ideal habitat conditions.

GREEN HAIRSTREAK *Callophrys rubi*

Flight season	JAN	FEB	MAR	APR	MAY	JUNE	JULY	AUG	SEPT	OCT	NOV	DEC

GREEN HAIRSTREAKS are the only British butterflies with truly green coloration on their wings. The combination of their small size, fast fluttering flight around scrub vegetation and coloration makes them difficult butterflies to find. As a result, they are almost certainly under-recorded. The undersides of the wings of both male and female are green with a faint white streak running parallel to the margins of fore- and hindwings. This streak varies in strength and can be almost absent in some individuals. In contrast, the uppersides are a dull velvet brown colour. At rest, or while nectaring, the wings are always held closed. In flight, the dull brown predominates, switching to a perfect green camouflage when it lands on a leaf or stem. There is little visible difference between male and female.

Typical green hairstreak habitat has a warm aspect with a mixture of scrub (often hawthorn) and sheltered open areas of grassland with good floral variety. Although there are many places with suitable foodplants, only a relatively few sites support a colony. There is almost certainly a more exacting habitat requirement, perhaps associated with ant populations, that is not yet understood. Of the British hairstreaks, this species flies earliest in the year, generally emerging in late April or early May and flying until mid- to late June.

Eggs are laid singly on a wide variety of plants, including gorse, broom, rock-rose, dogwood, bramble (the specific name *rubi* refers to the bramble) and several vetch species. On one particular local site, clear preference was shown for plants of dragon's-teeth

growing in relative abundance. The caterpillar hatches about two weeks after the eggs have been laid and feeds on the new growth of the plant, where the markings on its body provide excellent camouflage.

There is evidence that the caterpillar pupates within an ant nest, although little is known about the natural cycle of this species. Certainly the pupa is a uniform brown colour, which matches soil rather than vegetation. It has a sound organ used to emit squeaks audible to the human ear and believed to attract ants. Hibernation as a pupa lasts about nine months.

This species is recorded at quite a number of local sites, but is by no means common. Typical sites include several disused (and some active) railway cuttings, which seem to provide the right conditions, and it is most commonly found on scrubby areas of chalk and limestone grassland. The distribution map shows several strong locations on the Downs and Chilterns.

Green hairstreak caterpillar

Where the green hairstreak is found, colonies seem to be relatively stable, although numbers do fluctuate from year to year. Without more information on its exact habitat needs, it is difficult to know how best to protect and encourage this species. Like many other species it is probable that maintaining a sheltered mixed scrub/grassland structure on its known sites will provide the greatest benefit.

BROWN HAIRSTREAK *Thecla betulae*

JAN	FEB	MAR	APR	MAY	JUNE	JULY	AUG	SEPT	OCT	NOV	DEC

Flight season

THE BROWN HAIRSTREAK is the largest of our native hairstreaks and has a rather striking coloration, which is generally more vivid in the female. The undersides of the wings are predominantly orange-brown with relatively bold white streaks running across fore- and hindwings. There is also a very distinct tail on the hindwing. The uppersides of the male are deep brown with a slightly paler patch on each forewing. In contrast, the female has more strongly coloured undersides and a bright orange patch on each forewing, which is clearly visible when she basks in a sheltered sunny spot, often remaining there for long periods of time between egg-laying missions.

Female brown hairstreak basking in sunlight

This is a difficult species to find, even in its better colonies, which are usually spread over large areas with a very low density. It tends to fly around the tops of scrub with a short erratic spiralling flight. After some practice, it becomes easier to spot. In very warm weather it flies much more vigorously and over much greater distances, and is probably one of the more widely-ranging hairstreaks. After they emerge, males congregate around a high 'master tree', usually an ash, awaiting the arrival of newly emerged females. The males seldom leave the master tree, and feed mainly on honeydew deposits left by aphids. After mating, the female brown hairstreaks disperse to lay their eggs and will stop from time to time to nectar on flowers such as thistles, yarrow and fleabane.

Brown hairstreak egg

The brown hairstreak is one of the latest butterflies to emerge each year. It flies in late summer, emerging usually in late July or early August and flying until mid-September.

Long blackthorn hedgerows with new growth are favoured for egg-laying. Eggs are laid singly, after a careful assessment by the female butterfly, wandering methodically over the stems of the plant for a suitable site. The site chosen is almost invariably on the inside of the fork where a one-year old lateral twig shoots from a two-year old stem, and is usually within a metre of the ground. It is not uncommon to find more than one egg on a twig, but these are probably laid on separate occasions. The eggs are pure white slightly flattened spheres with a beautiful sculptured surface and are relatively easy to locate once you have seen the first one – but it may take a long and patient search to find the first!

The eggs overwinter and the caterpillar does not emerge until late spring. It feeds on the young growth of the blackthorn at dusk and into the night, remaining motionless under a leaf during the day. It is probably this slow method of feeding which accounts for its late emergence as an adult. In mid-June it moves to ground level, where it pupates.

Locally, this species is very uncommon. It requires extended lengths of blackthorn hedge in sheltered positions growing relatively wild and cut relatively infrequently, by traditional methods – preferably by hand. The currently commonplace use of mechanical flails and hedge trimmers does not provide the successional stages of hedge growth needed, with a good flush of new growth near to ground level, and as a result the number of suitable sites has dramatically declined. At its best local site, careful management has resulted in retention of a strong and stable colony.

PURPLE HAIRSTREAK *Quercusia quercus*

JAN	FEB	MAR	APR	MAY	JUNE	JULY	AUG	SEPT	OCT	NOV	DEC

Flight season

Male purple hairstreak

THE PURPLE HAIRSTREAK is probably our most common and widespread hairstreak, but it is one of the most difficult butterflies to spot. At close quarters it is very striking. The undersides of both male and female are a pale grey with strong white streak markings and small orange spots next to a short tail on the hindwing. The uppersides of the wings provide the striking surprise, being a uniform black colour. At a particular angle of illumination, the wings shine bright purple over most of their area on the male and over patches of the forewing on the female. This purple coloration of the wings is similar to that of the male purple emperor.

The problem when searching for the purple hairstreak is that it is a tree canopy species, usually flying around the tops of the mature oak trees that form its typical habitat. It has a typical 'hairstreak' flight, short, spiralling and erratic, which requires practice to identify. In flight it appears grey, from the colour of the undersides. After you 'get your eye in' to its flight pattern, however, it becomes easier to spot and often several can be seen around a single tree. The species flies in mid-summer, from late June to late July or early August.

Adult butterflies spend most of their time in the tree tops and seldom come down to ground level. This means that although it is not uncommon, it is difficult to study and its life-cycle is not well understood. Probably the best opportunity to observe an adult at close quarters is just after it has emerged from the pupa at ground level. The adults seldom nectar at flowers, and instead fuel on the sticky sweet honeydew deposits left on leaves by aphids.

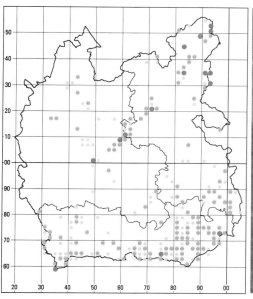

43

Eggs are laid in suitable mature oaks, between buds on the ends of twigs. The caterpillar develops fully within the egg, but overwinters before emerging. The oak is notable as a tree species for supporting more species of insect than any other in this country. The brown striped caterpillars feed on the developing buds. Little is known about pupation of this species, but pupae have been found in ants' nests on the ground under the outer edge of the tree canopy.

The distribution map for this species shows it to be fairly widespread. Although the pattern is patchy, that is almost certainly more due to the difficulties of recording it than to its actual absence. It is commonly found in mixed woodland sites with trees of varied age and a good structure of rides and clearings, such as are found particularly widely in east and south Berkshire and in the Vales of Oxford and Aylesbury, but also on the Chiltern woodlands.

Providing that reasonably large remnants of woodland remain and are managed to avoid becoming over-mature, the purple hairstreak seems to be at relatively little risk in this area. Much woodland managed primarily for pheasant rearing provides suitable conditions for this species, given reasonable care to maintain a natural structure of rides and glades with a succession of stages of tree development.

WHITE-LETTER HAIRSTREAK *Satyrium w-album*

Flight season

JAN	FEB	MAR	APR	MAY	JUNE	JULY	AUG	SEPT	OCT	NOV	DEC

WHITE-LETTER HAIRSTREAKS take both their scientific and common names from the characteristic white 'W' mark on the underside of their hindwings. Male and female butterflies are very similar. The ground colour of the underwings is a uniform grey-brown with a row of bold orange lunules outlined in black running continuously across the outer margin of the hindwing. The uppersides are a dull brown colour visible only in flight. There is a distinct tail. It is possible to confuse the white-letter hairstreak with the black hairstreak; however, the white-letter hairstreak is less bright in overall appearance and the 'W' marking on its underside is much more clearly formed.

The adults fly around the tree canopy, with a flight very similar to that of the purple hairstreak, but with a darker appearance. Unlike the purple hairstreak, they frequently come to ground level to nectar on flowers. Their favourites seem to be bramble and thistle flowers on which they may feed for long periods, moving occasionally from one flower to another nearby. If disturbed, they are likely to shoot off rapidly into or over the tree canopy.

White-letter hairstreaks emerge from late June to mid-July and the flight season lasts for about 4 or 5 weeks. The timing of the season varies by up to 2 weeks from year to year depending on the weather in spring.

44

The caterpillars of this species feed on elm, preferring wych elm. Pale green eggs, shaped like 'flying saucers', are laid in a sunny, sheltered position on the bark of twigs, often at the scar where the new growth joins growth from the previous year. The caterpillars are green with chevron stripes, and feed initially on the developing buds, later eating the leaves and pupating on a leaf or on a twig up in the tree.

The local distribution of this species shows no particularly strong pattern and, like the other hairstreaks, it is likely to be under-recorded. Because of its dependence on elm, white-letter hairstreak numbers were dramatically affected by the ravages of Dutch elm disease and for several years in the late 1970s and early 1980s there was widespread concern about the butterfly's viability. Recent years have been more encouraging. Although the disease is now widespread in Britain, the white-letter hairstreak has adapted from using mature elm trees to using the sucker growth which flourishes from the roots of diseased trees, before they reach the critical stage at which the disease takes effect. There has been a considerable recovery in numbers of the white-letter hairstreak recently and it is no longer seen as being under major threat. Although it is normally spotted in ones or twos, about 40 were recorded on one visit to a Berkshire BBONT reserve in 1992.

One locally strong site for the species, Maidenhead Thicket, has been dramatically affected by the construction of a wide and deep motorway cutting through the middle of the woodland area which included known breeding sites. The remaining area for this species has been reduced in size, but it is hoped that there is enough habitat left to allow the butterfly to remain viable on that site. The only redeeming feature of the change is that the chalky slopes of the new cutting may provide suitable habitat in the future for a variety of other butterfly species.

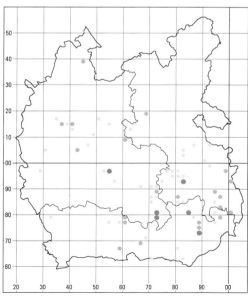

BLACK HAIRSTREAK *Satyrium pruni*

Flight season	JAN	FEB	MAR	APR	MAY	JUNE	JULY	AUG	SEPT	OCT	NOV	DEC

THE BLACK HAIRSTREAK is a small butterfly much sought after because of its very restricted geographical range. It is often described, unfairly, as being dull in colour. Male and female butterflies are similar in appearance, although the female tends to be slightly larger and a little more extensively coloured. At rest, the wings are always kept closed. The underside is an orange-brown colour, a little brighter than the underside of the white-letter hairstreak, and there is a white streak across fore- and hindwings. A broad orange crescent extends along the outer edge of the hindwing, fading into the forewing. There is a tail on the hindwing. Comparison of the photograph of this species with that of the white-letter hairstreak shows the key differences in the streak and the width of the orange crescent.

Black hairstreaks fly short distances in an acrobatic spiralling pattern, similar to that of the other hairstreaks, over and around the edges of the blackthorn scrub that forms its habitat. It is no wanderer, seldom straying very far from an established site, and will spend long periods of time sitting in the upper layers of the growth of blackthorn and nearby trees. The butterflies sometimes visit flowers of bramble and privet, but will more often feed on honeydew left by aphids on the leaves of trees.

Like the brown hairstreak, this species uses blackthorn and, very occasionally, wild plum as its foodplant, but unlike the former species, black hairstreaks use mature wood as well as new and can be found where there are fairly dense thickets bordering open rides. The butterflies emerge generally in mid- or late June. The flight season is short and

generally lasts only two to three weeks. A female adult will spend long periods of time moving along and around the stems, exploring with her abdomen to locate a suitable site for egg-laying. The eggs, laid on twigs between one and four years old, range in colour from pale yellow to brown and are much more difficult to find than those of the brown hairstreak.

The caterpillar forms within the egg but then enters hibernation, emerging in early spring to feed on the developing bud growth, when it has green and brown camouflage to match its surroundings. The pupa is supported on a twig of blackthorn with a silk strand round its middle, and closely resembles a bird dropping.

Black hairstreak pupa on a twig

Blackthorn is common and the precise habitat requirements restricting this species to its limited range are not fully understood. However, it is now thought that this area is one in which traditional woodland management with long coppice cycles (20–40 years) had been carried out continuously over many centuries, providing particularly suitable conditions for this very slow-moving butterfly. Elsewhere, in woodland with shorter coppice cycles (10–20 years), it was unable to move rapidly enough to recolonise new sites. Within its current range it can be found quite commonly; its typical habitat consists of large stands of blackthorn along sheltered, damp woodland rides and edges on heavy clay soils.

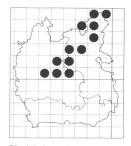

Black hairstreak records, 1975–1984

The UK range of this species is now restricted to a narrow strip running from north-east to south-west from Cambridgeshire into Oxfordshire. The map for this species shows clearly the south-west end of this distribution. The butterfly was first discovered in England as late as 1828, while the Bernwood colony was discovered only in 1918, by a schoolboy, W.F. Burrows, who was not believed at first until the discovery was verified. It has for some time now been established in north Buckinghamshire and on the border with Oxfordshire. Since 1984 several sites further south-west into Oxfordshire have been found (compare the survey map with that of 10 km square records for 1975–1984), but it is not clear whether this represents a true spread or is just a result of the more thorough recording during the atlas survey period.

The management of black hairstreak colonies requires very careful control of scrub growth and ride structure in its woodland sites. Many colonies have been lost since the widespread demise of traditional woodland management at the start of this century, and more will be lost if active measures are not taken to protect remaining sites. Most of these sites are now isolated to an extent whereby natural recolonisation is severely hindered.

The construction of the M40 extension in the late 1980s and the upgrading of the link road to Oxford led to the destruction of some of the local black hairstreak colonies in residual woodland. Where the M40 passes Bernwood Forest a remnant of land at the wood edge has been left and is now being managed specifically for conservation (see page 124). Close watch is being kept to see whether the butterfly can spread from neighbouring colonies established in the wood to form a new colony on planted blackthorn near to the wood edge.

SMALL COPPER *Lycaena phlaeas*

Flight season	JAN	FEB	MAR	APR	MAY	JUNE	JULY	AUG	SEPT	OCT	NOV	DEC

THE SMALL COPPER is a small but very attractive butterfly not uncommon in our local area. Apart from her larger size, the female of the species is very similar to the male. Both have bright and slightly metallic copper uppersides. The forewing has a dark edge and a pattern of black spots. The hindwing is dark with an orange band near the wing margin, sometimes with a row of blue spots on the dark area just inside the orange band. The undersides are also attractively coloured, although the hindwing is rather dull, providing camouflage when the butterfly is roosting.

When basking or nectaring, the wings are generally held in a half- to three-quarters open position and are seldom found fully open. They seem to have some preference for yellow flowers, and they are often seen nectaring on flowers of the daisy family, such as common fleabane. They can also be found in the garden nectaring on marjoram.

The male is fiercely territorial and will select a suitable vantage point on low vegetation. He will fly up to buzz any intruder, large or small, and chase it off before returning to the same spot again. This rapid flight makes it very difficult to follow the butterfly by eye and it is better to wait for it to return to its vantage point to observe it again. If a female enters his territory she is vigorously courted. Small coppers are quite wide-ranging and will move considerable distances to find suitable breeding sites.

The species has two and sometimes three broods each year. The broods are quite long-lasting and tend to overlap so that the butterfly may be seen for much of the period between April and October. Eggs are laid singly on leaves of the foodplant, usually common sorrel

or sheep's sorrel, in open rough grassland. The white eggs are a slightly flattened dome shape, and are covered with a honeycomb pattern. The green caterpillars, sometimes tinged with pink, feed on the leaves of the plant, eating grooves from the underside. Caterpillars from the last brood of the year go into hibernation in autumn.

The abundance of this species varies significantly from year to year. Relatively poor years in 1987 and 1988 were followed by two better years in 1989 and 1990, when summers were warm and numbers built up strongly, but numbers fell off again progressively in 1991 and 1992 (see table on page 15).

The distribution map shows this to be a successful and widespread species locally. It occupies a wide variety of grassland sites, ranging from chalk downs to wide field margins, overgrown set-aside farming land, wasteland and the verges of roads and footpaths, wherever its foodplant is abundant. Because of its very territorial behaviour, the small copper is usually seen in only ones and twos within a small area, although there are a few sites where much larger numbers have been seen.

SMALL BLUE *Cupido minimus*

JAN	FEB	MAR	APR	MAY	JUNE	JULY	AUG	SEPT	OCT	NOV	DEC

Flight season

THE SMALL BLUE really is small – it is the smallest of our British butterfly species – making it quite challenging to spot. There is little difference between the sexes, but individual adults can vary quite widely in size. Both sexes have dark uppersides, which vary from dark brown to blue-black, and the male has a slight dusting of blue scales near to the

49

Mating pair of small blues

Small blue caterpillar
feeding on kidney vetch
flower head

body. The undersides are a pale blue-grey with a pattern of small black spots roughly parallel to the outer wing margin. The wings are fringed with white scales. It has a rapid flight which makes it quite difficult to follow.

Despite its small size, the male aggressively defends its territory and courts females from a vantage point on a grass leaf where he will often spend long periods basking. Generally the butterfly remains within a rather small colony area, often only a few tens of metres in size, although a wanderer is occasionally found at a much greater distance.

Adult small blues emerge in mid-May, flying until late June. In this local area, there is often a small second brood of adults that fly in late summer. Pale bluish-white eggs are laid singly within the flower heads of the butterfly's sole foodplant, kidney vetch, and can be found quite easily with a little practice. The slug-shaped pale buff caterpillar feeds on the developing flower buds. It moves very slowly over the flower head, eating holes through into the buds, with its long thin head completely concealed inside. Its colour is a good match for the colour of the dry seed heads. The caterpillar hibernates at ground level and pupates early in the following spring.

The map shows this species to be most heavily concentrated in clusters of sites on the chalk grasslands of the Downs and Chilterns, but it occurs in good colonies on other areas, including limestone sites in north Oxfordshire. Sites range from widespread downland to small residues of habitat only a few square metres in size. There is a colony on the outskirts of Oxford, maintained by a very small area of kidney vetch on a short wide section of roadside verge, and another small colony on a disused sand quarry in south Oxfordshire. On the chalk, colonies are found in most places where the foodplant occurs in reasonably sheltered sites. Several of the colonies are within BBONT reserves. In many places, colonies survive where relatively few foodplants are found. Indeed, it seems to prefer locations where there are dispersed plants rather than dense concentrations.

The local status of the small blue appears to be reasonably stable where the right grassland conditions occur, but its requirements are not well-known, so its security can not be taken for granted. The availability of the foodplant is obviously crucial and its loss by cultivation, overgrazing or shading out by scrub will lead to the loss of colonies of the butterfly.

SILVER-STUDDED BLUE *Plebejus argus*

Flight season

JAN	FEB	MAR	APR	MAY	JUNE	JULY	AUG	SEPT	OCT	NOV	DEC

SILVER-STUDDED BLUES have wings which are more rounded than those of the common blue. The male has a very rich blue upperside and the wings have a broad black border edged with white. The female normally has brown uppersides with faint orange markings along the margins, although some are found with extensive blue on the uppersides. The undersides are similar to those of the common blue. At very close quarters one of the key features can be seen: some of the black spots along the outer row on the underside of the hindwing have scales in the centre which gleam silvery-blue in sunlight. These vary considerably between individuals and are virtually absent in some.

Locally, this is a species of heathland and has a very marginal distribution in southern Berkshire overlapping into the more extensive heaths of Surrey and Hampshire. It shares many of these habitats with the grayling, also a heathland species. Adults fly weakly and cover only short distances. Their preferred habitat consists of areas of heather, especially where there is new growth with bare ground, and they may be found nectaring on the flowers.

Silver-studded blue is single brooded with adults flying from late June into mid-August. Although this overlaps with the flight season of the common blue, the silver-studded blue tends to dominate on those sites where it occurs.

Silver-studded blue on cross-leaved heath

In this country, eggs are laid on a variety of foodplants, including trefoils and common rock-rose. In the heathland habitats where it occurs in this local area, eggs are laid on young shoots of heathers, including *Calluna vulgaris* and *Erica* species, and on gorse. The caterpillar does not emerge until the following spring. Sites are chosen where there is regenerating growth interspersed with patches of bare soil. In these sheltered but open spots, local temperatures rise rapidly in sunlight, allowing the caterpillar to feed and develop quickly. The caterpillar has the same slug-like shape as other lycaenids and is green with a brown stripe down its back. This species has a close, but not fully understood, association with ants, which are rewarded for their attentions with secretions of sugary liquid. The pupa is normally formed inside an ant nest. When the butterfly emerges, its body is covered with sugary liquid which attracts attendant ants as it extends its wings.

The extensive areas of mostly pine plantation and forest lying between Ascot and Sandhurst support a number of colonies. Some colonies are on open heathland sites (such

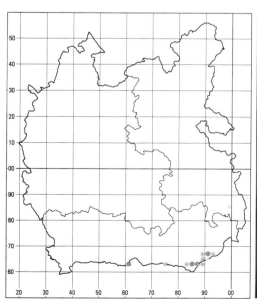

as Owlsmoor Bog) where the habitat has remained suitable by a combination of conservation management, Ministry of Defence activity and fires, for the most part unintentional. The latter have often been extensive summer burns when the vegetation is dry and have probably damaged as many sites as they have benefited. In some instances, fires have kept birch and pine regeneration in check. Ideally, management by fire should be restricted to small areas in any one year to create a mosaic of habitats. At some sites, silver-studded blue numbers have fallen very low in recent years, but there is a chance that populations will increase where burnt areas regenerate a suitable heather flora and ant fauna.

Within the Ascot to Sandhurst forest area, some silver-studded blue colonies have been discovered inhabiting wide heathy rides and tracks. Conservation work has been aimed at improving these habitats. Initiatives to link such habitats through the ride system should encourage dispersal to new areas as habitat becomes suitable. Odd individuals have occurred at nearby sites, such as Englemere Pond, where future management aims to extend the small patches of heath to benefit this and other species. BBONT, Crown Estates and Bracknell Forest Borough Council are all managing sites with this species in mind.

BROWN ARGUS *Aricia agestis*

Flight season	JAN	FEB	MAR	APR	MAY	JUNE	JULY	AUG	SEPT	OCT	NOV	DEC

THE BROWN ARGUS is the odd one out of the blues, in that neither male nor female butterflies have any blue coloration. The uppersides of both are a rich chocolate brown. The wings of the female have a row of bold orange spots along the margins of the

uppersides. In the male, these spots fade away towards the upper half of the forewing. The underside is similar to that of the common blue, although the markings are somewhat neater and bolder. They spend much time basking or nectaring on a variety of flowers with their wings fully open.

This is a species of predominantly chalk and limestone habitats where its foodplant, common rock-rose, is reasonably abundant. It has a fast and slightly erratic flight low over the ground, making it difficult to follow, in contrast to the more fluttering flight of the common blue. It wanders quite extensively and may be found occasionally some distance from suitable habitats.

The species is double-brooded, flying from early May to mid-June and again from mid-July to mid-September. The brown argus lays its green-white eggs on the leaves (usually the undersides) of rock-rose, preferring plants growing in sheltered sunny positions. Where rock-rose is not available, the butterfly has been known to lay eggs on common stork's-bill and related *Geranium* species. The pale green slug-shaped caterpillar feeds on the softer tissues on the underside of the leaf, leaving the top layer intact. The pupa is formed at ground level. Caterpillars of the second brood enter hibernation in autumn and recommence feeding in the spring.

The distribution map for the brown argus shows the predominance of colonies on the chalk of the Downs and Chilterns. There are also many other sites in the area at which suitable foodplants occur, particularly in mid-Oxfordshire and north Buckinghamshire, often where there are small local outcrops of limestone with ancient grassland. Some of the single sightings may be accidental occurrences of wandering individuals.

The foodplant of this butterfly is vulnerable to agricultural operations, including both ploughing and fertiliser application, and grows best on reasonably fertile soils, which are most likely to be suitable for agriculture. The brown argus could decline drastically in its distribution as development marches on and, if we are not careful, may end up being confined to a small number of nature reserves.

Underside of female brown argus

COMMON BLUE *Polyommatus icarus*

JAN	FEB	MAR	APR	MAY	JUNE	JULY	AUG	SEPT	OCT	NOV	DEC

Flight season

THE COMMON BLUE is the most widespread and adaptable of our blue species. Anyone seeing a blue butterfly in mid-summer is most likely to be looking at a common blue. The male has bright blue uppersides with a thin black line and a uniform white margin to the wings. The female butterfly varies greatly from dull brown with rather indistinct orange spots to a strong blue with orange spots along the wing margins. The undersides are patterned with black spots and orange lunules along the wing margins.

53

Common blue egg-laying on common bird's-foot-trefoil

Common blues are found in open grassland, in large clearings and rides in woodland and on wide roadside verges, flying quite vigorously low over the ground. Males generally emerge several days before the females and set up territories in advance, ready to mate with females very soon after they emerge. The butterflies spend much time basking and nectaring in the sun and are easily found in the morning basking in preparation for flight. In the late afternoon or early evening, they retire to roost and can be seen 'asleep' perched upside-down high on a grass stem. In the garden, they often choose to nectar and roost on the flowers of lavender.

The common blue has two, or occasionally three, broods a year. The white eggs are laid singly on its foodplant, which is usually common bird's-foot-trefoil, although black medick and other trefoils are sometimes used. The green caterpillars have the characteristic slug-like shape of the blue butterfly caterpillars, but are not strongly marked. At first, they eat only the soft tissues of the underside of the leaf, leaving the upper tough membrane intact. Later, they eat the whole leaf. The pupa is normally formed at ground level and, like other blues, is often tended by ants, although common blues do not have such a close association with ants as some other blue species. Caterpillars from the last brood of the year overwinter at a partially developed stage and complete their growth the following spring.

The common blue is very widely distributed and was recorded in over half of the tetrad squares during the atlas period. It is frequently found in medium-quality wild grassland, on waste ground, disused quarries and railway lines and on set-aside land. Its occurrence on agricultural land depends on there being wide field margins or pockets of wild habitat in which it can breed. In the countryside generally, its favourite foodplant is common and widespread, so that the common blue's status as our most regularly abundant blue butterfly seems to be reasonably secure.

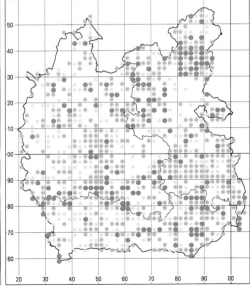

CHALKHILL BLUE *Lysandra coridon*

JAN	FEB	MAR	APR	MAY	JUNE	JULY	AUG	SEPT	OCT	NOV	DEC

Flight season

THE MALE CHALKHILL BLUE has striking pale blue uppersides, which appear almost silver in flight, with dark margins. The edges of the wings are fringed in white, crossed by black lines along the end of each vein. The paleness of the male makes it hard to confuse with other blue species. The female is a different matter. Her brown uppersides, with faint orange marginal spots, are nearly identical to those of the female Adonis blue (apart from the lack of blue near the body and the outer edges of the hindwings) and awkwardly similar to those of the female common blue. Common blue females can be recognised by the unbroken white band around the wing edges and the greater extent of blue scaling across the uppersides

The undersides of the chalkhill and the Adonis blue are very similar, although those of the latter tend to be darker with more pronounced orange markings. Worn specimens often prove impossible to distinguish in the field.

Though chalkhill blue caterpillars may occasionally feed on common bird's-foot-trefoil, only horseshoe vetch seems able to sustain it for several generations. Unfortunately for the butterfly, horseshoe vetch is a fussy plant. It does best on poor quality chalk and limestone soils that have sufficiently sparse vegetation for it to compete and survive. Any form of agricultural 'improvement' will increase the growth of grasses and other coarser plants, which eventually overwhelm the vetch. On the other hand, if an owner decides that these downlands are of such little agricultural value that he will not farm them at all, then the vetch is shaded out as encroaching scrub thickens.

Male chalkhill blue nectaring on a pyramidal orchid

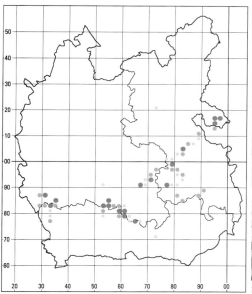

55

Female chalkhill blue

Chalkhill blue egg on
horseshoe vetch

Consequently there are few sites ideally suited to the foodplant. Of these, even fewer are acceptable to the butterfly. Where the turf is too high or too dense, ground conditions will not be warm enough for the caterpillars to complete their growth in time. This means that in the local area, the butterfly will lay eggs only on vetch plants growing on south-facing slopes if the turf is less than about 12 cm high, and on north-west facing slopes if the turf is less than 6 cm high. Additionally, females prefer sites near the tops of slopes and in the vicinity of ants' nests, interspersed with areas of longer turf for roosting.

These habitat requirements can be maintained by grazing, but the correct balance is difficult to achieve. The effect of 'wild' grazing by rabbits and deer must be assessed and then stock can be used to augment this effect. Winter grazing is most beneficial, especially by heavy stock which break up the ground. Summer grazing is disadvantageous as it leads to the horseshoe vetch, and presumably any caterpillars on it, being eaten. However, light summer grazing is preferable to none at all, in the long term. It allows vetch to survive at low densities, from which it recovers more quickly than many of its competitors, once grazing pressure is relaxed.

The chalkhill blue is single brooded, with adults emerging in late July and August. Males emerge before females and are the first to fly each day. When females emerge, they release pheromones that attract patrolling males and many are fertilised before their wings have dried. Once fertilised, they reject male advances by flicking their wings open and crawling down into the vegetation, or by flying strongly upwards.

Apart from sorties to find nectar and patches of horseshoe vetch, females rarely fly. Mostly, they crawl through the undergrowth, often deep in vegetation and completely out of the sun. This explains their apparent scarcity even when males fly in hundreds. When they do find suitable foodplants, they 'taste' them with their feet before laying eggs on or around the plant.

The eggs overwinter and caterpillars hatch the following May. At first, they feed entirely on the undersides of the leaves, creating small opaque 'windows', moving on as they grow to eat discs from the leaf edges and later feeding on entire leaves and flower buds. Feeding activity peaks around dusk and dawn. At these times, the larvae are normally surrounded by attentive ants, whom they feed with sticky protein-rich secretions, presumably in return for protection from predators. When they finish feeding, the caterpillars hide under stones or crawl down amongst roots and the ants leave them. Caterpillars are normally fully grown by the third week of June. Pupation occurs under stones or in the soil, and lasts for about a month.

Nationally, the chalkhill blue is far less widespread than in previous centuries. Once it was found as far north as Lancashire in the west and Lincolnshire in the east. Collectors took many hundreds of specimens from these sites year upon year, apparently without much effect upon the colony size. Then, fairly suddenly, many famous colonies disappeared. Now the biggest colonies are in central southern counties and the Chilterns mark the northern limit. The distribution map shows the butterfly almost entirely confined to the chalk of the Downs and Chilterns, where they occur on the steeper slopes. Many colonies are found on the less favoured north-west or north-east slopes, because south facing slopes tend to be less steep and have been ploughed. The densest colonies are found where downland still exists on south facing slopes.

Nearly all the big colonies are on nature reserves, because of the expensive management required to keep invasive scrub at bay. Traditional grazing, which kept hillsides 'open' for centuries, disappeared in the harsher economic climate between and after the world wars. Simultaneously, rabbits populations were greatly reduced by myxomatosis. Large sections of downland were left to scrub over or were planted by the Forestry Commission, leaving only remnant populations of horseshoe vetch and chalkhill blue around footpaths such as the Ridgeway, where walkers trampled the turf to an acceptable condition.

This contraction in range continued until the late 1980s. Then a rebuilding of rabbit numbers, coupled with a better understanding of habitat management, began to stem and even turn the tide at many sites in the early 1990s. The chalkhill blue spread back to sites it had left in the early 1980s; on one site in the Chilterns, a single vagrant female in 1990 led to about 15 adults in 1991 and slightly more in 1992. Over the same period, occasional wandering males were seen far from known colonies (note the single sighting in the middle of the Vale of Aylesbury).

Further hope for the future management of sites is offered by the Countryside Stewardship Scheme. It compensates farmers who safeguard the landscape, for instance by using traditional grazing on unproductive land, and many landowners in the three counties are returning to farming methods that should suit the vetch and the butterfly.

ADONIS BLUE *Lysandra bellargus*

JAN	FEB	MAR	APR	MAY	JUNE	JULY	AUG	SEPT	OCT	NOV	DEC	Flight season

THE ADONIS BLUE is the most vivid of the blue butterflies. The uppersides of the wings of the male are an electric, iridescent blue when the sun strikes them and, where they occur, individual basking males can often be seen, gleaming in the grass like jewels, from over 10 m away. The female is a dull grey-brown colour, very similar to the chalkhill blue female, making them very difficult to distinguish, particularly since all the local Adonis blue sites also have chalkhill blue colonies and there is an overlap in their flight seasons in August. Both male and female have black markings at the end of each vein in the white wing fringes.

The undersides of both male and female are also very similar to those of the chalkhill blue, but tend to be significantly darker in overall coloration. The caterpillars of the two species share the same foodplant, horseshoe vetch, on which eggs are laid singly, but the Adonis blue is even more fussy about the choice of site. In this local area, the Adonis blue is very much at the northern limit of its range, and can survive only where conditions are ideal. This means steep south-facing slopes where the chalk vegetation is very short and,

Male Adonis blues basking amongst horseshoe vetch

in strong sunshine, the ground temperatures reach as much as 20–30°C higher than shade temperatures. It therefore shares also with chalkhill blue most of its strict habitat requirements and very similar site management requirements and problems.

Adults also use horseshoe vetch as a source of nectar, along with marjoram, trefoils and other downland flowers. Males emerge several days before females and range quite widely over the colony area to set up territories, mating with newly-emerged females as soon as they appear, in very much the same way as chalkhill blues. The inconspicuous females are much less in evidence and spend most of their time crawling around foodplants at ground level or nectaring.

In contrast to the chalkhill blue, Adonis blues are double-brooded, with the first adult brood flying mainly in late May and early June. The second brood flies in late summer, generally into September. Its greater selectivity of suitable sites presumably stems from the more exacting needs of getting through two generations in each season. Eggs are laid on the foodplant, with strong preference for small plants growing in very open short turf. Like other blues, the young caterpillars feed on the undersides of the leaves, progressing to eating whole leaves by the time they are fully grown. The caterpillars of the second brood go into hibernation in autumn.

The species again has a strong association with ants, which seem to provide the caterpillar with protection, in exchange for sweet secretions from its skin. It is likely also that the ants protect the pupa by taking it underground into the ant nest. This aspect of its biology is not yet fully understood and there may well be factors involved, such as association with a particular ant species, that are critical to its survival within a particular habitat. Pupae are formed around ground level and are indeed found in ant nests, presumably having been carried there by the ants.

Although the Adonis blue was recorded from two sites in Buckinghamshire early during the atlas survey period, it is now feared to have become extinct there, because of a combination of marginal weather conditions and problems in maintaining balanced grazing regimes. On one site, there was evidence of overgrazing by horses in dry summers when herb and grass growth was slow, which probably damaged the foodplant. It now seems to be confined to just a handful of sites on steeply sloping chalk grasslands on the Oxfordshire/Berkshire border, and must be considered vulnerable even there. The future of this species in our local area is indeed threatened, much more so than the chalkhill blue, and special measures may be required to protect these last colonies.

HOLLY BLUE *Celastrina argiolus*

JAN	FEB	MAR	APR	MAY	JUNE	JULY	AUG	SEPT	OCT	NOV	DEC

Flight season

T HE HOLLY BLUE is the earliest blue butterfly of the year and, in good years, is sometimes flying by late March. However, it cannot always be found, since this is a 'boom and bust' species, with numbers varying dramatically from year to year.

Both the male and female butterflies have bright blue uppersides with a rather rounded wing shape. The female has a broad black band bordering the forewings and extending onto the hindwings, in contrast to the very narrow black band found on the male.

In flight, this species can be confused with the common blue, although its habits are different – holly blues tend to fly up high round shrubs and trees, whereas common blues usually fly much closer to ground level. At rest, the holly blue is much easier to identify.

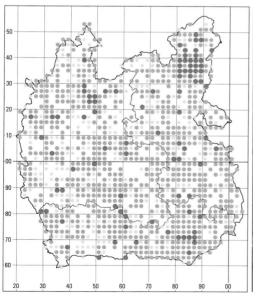

59

Parasitic wasp,
Listrodomus nycthemerus,
newly emerged

The undersides are a uniform pale blue, marked with very fine black spots and dash marks and are quite different to any of the other blue butterflies, except the small blue.

The holly blue is double-brooded, and each brood uses a different foodplant. The spring brood lays eggs on flowers of holly (hence the butterfly's name), whilst the summer brood, which flies in July and August, lays mainly on ivy flowers. In both cases, the caterpillar feeds on the highly nutritious developing flower buds, moving slowly over the flower head and eating a small opening in the side of a bud. It has a small elongated head which it pushes fully into the bud. Occasionally other plants, including dogwood and snowberry, are used. In the very warm summer of 1989, when there were large numbers of holly blues, they were seen laying on very unusual plants including heather, purple loosestrife and even buddleia. In long hot seasons adults have been seen flying until October, possibly from a weak third brood. The second brood enters hibernation at the pupal stage.

During the atlas survey period, there were very large changes in the abundance of this species. It was previously seen in good numbers locally in 1984. There were very few seen in 1987 and 1988 (recorded in only 5% of surveyed squares each year), but numbers grew dramatically the following year. They were recorded in 27% of squares in 1989, and in 59% in 1990 and 1991. The population then began to decline, dropping to 27% of recorded squares in 1992. By 1993, they had all but disappeared again, being seen in only about 2% of recorded sites (see also page 104).

These dramatic changes in abundance are typical of the holly blue, which is one of the most widespread butterfly species in the world. There are various theories, none of which are proven, for these changes. One theory relates to a parasitic ichneumon wasp, *Listrodomus nycthemerus*, which is specific to the holly blue and lays its eggs in the body of the young caterpillar. The parasite larva feeds inside the caterpillar and the adult develops and emerges only after the caterpillar has pupated (see photograph). In cases where the parasite is specific to the host, the population dynamics of parasite and host will be linked – when the butterfly becomes plentiful, then the parasite population will grow. If the parasite reaches high numbers then the population of the host will be dramatically reduced, leading in turn to a drastic drop in parasite numbers. With the holly blue, however, it is possible that the effect is much more complex than this simple theory alone would suggest.

Apart from these dramatic rises and falls in population, the holly blue is a widespread species, seen in many different habitats, but with a significant preference for wood edges and hedgerows, especially where there are bramble flowers to nectar on. It is also a species that frequents the garden, where it prefers shrubby areas and hedges, and was widely reported from many gardens during its recent years of abundance. Apart from the natural forces that seem to dictate its numbers, this butterfly seems not to be threatened to any significant extent in this area and we look forward to seeing it in larger numbers again in a few years time.

THE METALMARKS

THE METALMARKS were once classed by a number of authorities as a separate family of butterflies, the Riodinidae. It is now classified by some modern taxonomists as a sub-family, the Riodininae, of the family Lycaenidae.

There is only one European representative of the metalmarks, the Duke of Burgundy. A few other species of metalmarks are found in Asia, Africa and North America, but most of them occur in tropical South America. These species have a very wide variety of shape and colouring and many examples of mimicry. Some have metallic markings on the wings, giving rise to the common name of this sub-family. This variety makes our only local species rather dull by comparison. Seen from our local context, however, this species has some fascinating features.

In common with the other metalmarks, the Duke of Burgundy seems to occupy an interesting position in the evolutionary development of butterflies. The forelegs of the female are small but fully developed, with a total of seven segments and a claw at the end, and are used for walking. Those of the male are reduced to a total of only three segments without a claw. They are not used at all and are simply held retracted against the body. This feature distinguishes the Duke of Burgundy from the rest of the Lycaenidae, where all six legs are fully deployed. This is part way to the Nymphalidae, where the forelegs are reduced in all individuals, male and female. At very close quarters, this particular feature makes it possible to determine the sex of adult Duke of Burgundy butterflies.

DUKE OF BURGUNDY *Hamearis lucina*

Flight season

JAN	FEB	MAR	APR	MAY	JUNE	JULY	AUG	SEPT	OCT	NOV	DEC

Underside of male
Duke of Burgundy

THE DUKE OF BURGUNDY is a small but aggressive butterfly which has undergone serious decline with many local extinctions in recent years. It is now more or less restricted to nature reserves with grassland or woodland habitats.

This species was formerly known as the 'Duke of Burgundy fritillary', because it has chequered orange and brown markings on the uppersides and also 'pearl' markings on the undersides, so characteristic of the fritillary species of the Nymphalidae. It is not, however, related to these species and the term 'fritillary' is no longer used in formal descriptions. Incidentally, no-one seems to know exactly why it is called 'Duke of Burgundy' – it may be a dated political reference to the pugnacious behaviour of this small butterfly.

Male Duke of Burgundy butterflies are strongly territorial. They take up position on a prominent grass leaf or other convenient vantage point in a sunny sheltered location above ground level. This is where they are usually spotted, basking with their wings open in the sunshine. They fly up rapidly to chase off any intruder, returning to the same point a few minutes later. If another male enters the territory, they will spiral round together until one of them concedes and flies off. The females are much more discreet in their behaviour and spend most of their time in the undergrowth searching out suitable food-plants. They do not spend much time nectaring, but do occasionally visit hawthorn flowers.

The Duke of Burgundy is single-brooded and emerges between the beginning of May and mid-June, the males emerging a few days earlier than the females. The average life span of an individual adult is only 5–7 days.

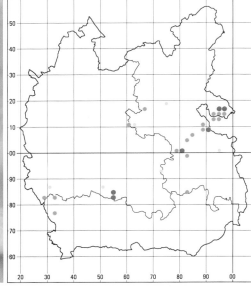

The foodplants used for egg laying depend on the habitat. In the more common grassland colonies, cowslip is used. In woodland habitats, primrose is used. In both cases, plants are chosen that are vigorously growing in sunny, sheltered positions, but partially shaded by long grass so that the leaves remain green and fleshy through the caterpillars' development stages. In open grassland with short turf, cowslips become dry and wither badly in strong sunshine and therefore cannot sustain the caterpillars.

Eggs are laid in small groups, ranging from one to as many as ten, though more usually two to four, on the undersides of the foodplant leaves. After carefully choosing a suitable plant, the female butterfly perches on the edge of the leaf, curling her abdomen underneath to lay within about 1 cm of the edge. The eggs are rather pear-shaped spheres and are glossy white in colour. Shortly before the caterpillar hatches, the hairs on its developing body form a criss-cross 'fishnet' pattern showing through the egg shell. They eat part of the eggshell to make a way out, and most of the remainder after they emerge.

Typical feeding pattern of Duke of Burgundy caterpillars on cowslip

The brown hairy caterpillars, similar in shape to, but not quite as slug-like as, those of the blues, eat out panels between the veins of the leaf in a rather neat patchwork fashion, which makes their presence on a plant rather easy to deduce in mid-summer. This provides a convenient way of establishing that a colony exists on a particular site outside of the flight season. Slugs and snails also eat cowslip and primrose leaves, but they are untidy by comparison, tearing at the leaves and leaving them ragged and slimy.

Locally, the distribution of the Duke of Burgundy is mainly on the chalk grasslands of the Downs and Chilterns, with weak woodland colonies, some of the last in Britain, on the Buckinghamshire/Oxfordshire border. Virtually all remaining sites are on nature reserves. Previously, colonies were also found on several limestone grassland sites in north Oxfordshire (see the map of 1975–1984 10 km square records), but these all seem to be extinct now. The best habitats with the strongest colonies are where there is a mixture of open grassland, sheltered by partial scrub or woodland. This is a successional stage in the degeneration of open grassland and is therefore transient unless actively managed. The most successful management for suitable sites seems to be to cut scrub back in pockets, leaving small, open but sheltered clearings with initially bare soil patches where the foodplant has an opportunity to germinate. Heavy grazing, for example by sheep on farmed land, or by rabbits, will remove the foodplant itself and the longer grasses needed to partially shade the plants, and the butterfly will be unable to breed successfully.

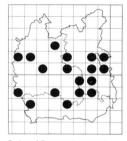

Duke of Burgundy records, 1975–1984

One site on the Downs has a particularly large colony of Duke of Burgundy butterflies and scrub management carried out over the last 2–3 years by Butterfly Conservation seems to be benefiting this species. A transect recording route is now being walked regularly there to monitor the effectiveness of the habitat management.

In woodland habitats, the management requirements are similar in their objectives – to maintain rides and clearings with a succession of vigorous primrose plants to provide suitable breeding and feeding sites. Primroses will normally survive for many years under the tree canopy, but grow vigorously only very early in the year, when the trees are still bare and sunlight reaches the ground. By the time the butterfly has emerged, these positions have become heavily shaded and are therefore quite unsuitable as breeding locations. It is when these areas are exposed by ride or clearing cutting that good persistently sunny conditions become available for egg-laying and caterpillar development, but these suitable conditions last for a few years only. Like so many other butterfly species, traditional woodland management by regular coppicing provides a succession of conditions that suit this species best.

It is almost certainly the lack of maintenance of these critical habitat conditions, following long-term changes in grazing patterns on grassland sites or the decline of coppicing activities in woodland, that has led to the loss of this species from so many of its former local sites. The necessary management tasks are generally more labour-intensive in woodland than on downland sites and suitable habitat conditions seem to decline more rapidly in woodlands where the soil is richer in nutrients and plant growth is generally more vigorous. This may explain why we have lost so many more of the woodland colonies. On those sites where Duke of Burgundy still remains, active management must be maintained to keep the site conditions near to optimum or further local extinctions will be inevitable.

VANESSIDS AND FRITILLARIES

THE NYMPHALIDAE family contains some of the largest and most flamboyant of the local butterfly species, along with a group now classified as a sub-family of the Nymphalidae, the Satyrinae, or browns, which are described separately in the following chapter. The Nymphalidae share a common physiological feature – the front pair of legs in the adult is reduced to a point where they are completely redundant as limbs and both male and female walk on only four legs. The small vestigial front legs of the male are covered in hair-like scales, so that they resemble brushes, and hence the group is also known as the 'brush-foot' family. The caterpillars of the vanessids and fritillaries are all spiny.

The family includes some of the most widespread and some of the most localised of species, some that have become more common and some hovering on the verge of extinction. In this chapter, the vanessids and fritillaries are described.

THE VANESSIDS include the well known and colourful 'garden' butterflies: small tortoiseshell, red admiral, peacock, comma and painted lady. Apart from the painted lady, which uses thistle, these 'garden' species use nettle as the foodplant and therefore can adapt well to man's activities. Large tortoiseshells are recorded only occasionally now, probably as migrants, and there are thought not to be any established colonies remaining in the UK.

THE FRITILLARIES share two common features, the orange and black chequered markings on the uppersides of their wings and the alarming fact that all are threatened – in the local area, one species has already become extinct within the last decade or so. Apart from one species (marsh fritillary), their caterpillars all feed on violet leaves and they are all single-brooded.

The name 'fritillary' comes from the Latin *fritillus*, meaning dice-box, a reference to the chequered marking (also found on the flowers of the snake's-head fritillary plant, another interesting rarity found locally on a few remaining unimproved flood meadows of the River Thames).

The increasing rarity of the fritillaries is a reflection of the specialised habitats they require, which are disappearing fast with the enormous changes in land management practices of the post-war years. It seems unlikely that very much can be done to reverse this decline, and we will do well to hold on to those fragile colonies that remain.

WHITE ADMIRAL *Ladoga camilla*

Flight season	JAN	FEB	MAR	APR	MAY	JUNE	JULY	AUG	SEPT	OCT	NOV	DEC

THE WHITE ADMIRAL is one of the most beautiful and spectacular butterflies of woodland. As it flies in the dappled sunlight, it is one of the most fascinating butterflies to watch – short periods of fluttering are interspersed with elegant gliding flight over a surprising distance. It is a species of rather untidy woodland and is found mainly in sheltered and rather shady rides. The origin of its curious name is discussed under its near namesake, the red admiral.

The white admiral has bold white markings on a very rich black-brown background, and these markings show clearly in flight. The margins of the wings are decorated with scalloped white fringes. When it settles, the undersides are spectacular in their own right, with their combination of bold white, orange-brown and pale blue markings (shown on page 5). There is little difference between male and female, the latter being just slightly larger. The white admiral can be confused with the purple emperor, but the underside markings are quite different and the purple emperor is larger and has plain margins and eyespots on its wings.

White admirals are single-brooded and fly between mid-June and mid-August. The life-cycle of this species is described in detail in the introductory part of this book (see page 4), and therefore only the salient features are given here. The beautifully sculptured eggs are laid singly in mid-summer on the edge of straggly strands of honeysuckle hanging at the shady edges of narrow rides. The caterpillar eats in a very characteristic way, starting at the tip of the leaf and eating on either side of the central leaf vein.

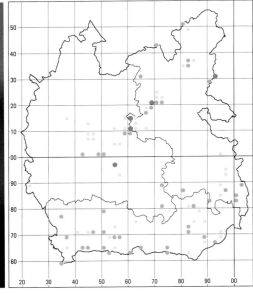

As autumn approaches, the partly-grown caterpillar constructs a shelter for hibernation within a partly-eaten leaf, emerging again the following spring to resume feeding. The fully grown caterpillar has an aggressive appearance, with bright green uppersides matching the leaf colour, deep red undersides matching the honeysuckle stem and spiny bristles in clumps along its body. When it is disturbed, it arches its back to intimidate predators.

It pupates in late spring, suspended from the underside of a convenient stem. The pupa has a complex shape, coloured green and brown, with gold markings, the overall effect resembling a fresh bird dropping hanging from the stem.

Nectaring white admirals are most frequently found on bramble blossom, their most favoured flower, and can frequently be seen in twos and threes in a woodland ride. When disturbed, they will often fly up into or over the tree canopy and will flutter and glide out of sight. They often sit tantalisingly high up in the canopy, basking in sunlight.

The white admiral has become much more widespread during this century. This is almost certainly due to the reduction in woodland management, especially post-war, producing the more 'neglected' woodland conditions where it seems to thrive. Honeysuckle (or woodbine) is traditionally the sign of a badly kept woodland; a woodman worthy of his trade kept his trees free from this plant. As such management has declined, honeysuckle has spread and suitable conditions for this species have become much more common, enabling the butterfly to expand its range. The main localities in this area are in the damp woodlands on the clays of the Vales of Aylesbury and Oxford, in north Buckinghamshire and in east and west Berkshire. In many of these woodlands, it can be quite commonplace, and much easier to spot than the purple emperor.

Although the current status of the white admiral seems to be relatively healthy in comparison with many other woodland butterflies, its continued survival in the long term cannot be taken for granted. As neglected woodland continues to decline, it will become over-mature, rides will close in, the ground will become shaded out completely and suitable conditions for the butterfly will disappear. It is therefore in the longer-term interests of this butterfly to seek to continue with traditional woodland management techniques wherever conservation resources allow.

PURPLE EMPEROR *Apatura iris*

JAN	FEB	MAR	APR	MAY	JUNE	JULY	AUG	SEPT	OCT	NOV	DEC	Flight season

POSSIBLY THE MOST ELUSIVE of the butterflies in this area, the purple emperor is often searched for but is frustratingly difficult to find. In mid-summer, people are often to be seen in the rides of Bernwood, walking and waiting patiently for an opportunity to see this magnificent butterfly. It is a rare butterfly anyway, but is all the more elusive simply because it is a species of the tree canopy and seldom visits ground level. It is more likely to be spotted soaring and gliding above the tree tops.

67

Underside of purple
emperor

The purple emperor is one of our largest butterflies. The female is a little larger than the male and has slightly more pronounced white patches on the uppersides of the wings. Both sexes have a small orange ring, an 'eye-mark', towards the bottom corner of the hindwing, which is a key distinction separating this species from the otherwise very similar white admiral.

The splendour of the male purple emperor is its most distinctive feature. When its wings are open at a suitable angle to the sun, an optical interference effect in very fine lines in the scale structure make them reflect a vivid purple-blue colour extending over most of the wing area. This type of wing colouring appears at its most spectacular in the unrelated Morpho butterflies of the tropics, where it is believed to assist in mutual recognition in the dense foliage of the tree canopy. It is notable that another of our tree canopy species, the purple hairstreak, to some extent shares this coloration and presumably these British species use the bright colour to assist recognition in the same way. The undersides of purple emperors are very boldly coloured with an eyespot marking which may help to discourage more nervous predators from attacking.

This butterfly does not seem to nectar and is not seen visiting flowers. It takes its nourishment from the honeydew of aphids and also from tree-sap exuded by wounds in tree trunks. The male, however, does come to ground level, where he will spend long periods of time at puddles, on animal droppings, 'licking' dry stones and even car windscreens. This probably enables the male to replenish salts lost in mating and is a form of behaviour found in many other species. It is also said that they are attracted to rotting flesh – pundits used to recommend trailing a long-dead rabbit carcass along forest rides to attract them down! When it does come down to ground, the butterfly is remarkably tame and can be approached much more easily than most other species.

Male purple emperors set up territories on 'master trees', often mature oak trees, rising above the canopy of rather open woodland, from which they fend off rival males and seek out females. The complex way in which these master trees are used and the life-cycle of this fascinating butterfly are described in detail by Ken Wilmott (see Bibliography, page 135).

Eggs are laid on the leaves of goat willow and grey willow, which are the foodplants in this country. The caterpillar has a fat body tapering to a point at the rear, whilst at the front, it has a pair of long 'horns', similar to those of a snail. In its early stages, it is brown. It hibernates as a partly-grown caterpillar. In later stages, it is green with faint yellow chevrons and is very difficult to find.

The purple emperor now occurs in only a scattering of colonies in the larger blocks of old woodland still left in this area. Its main stronghold is in the complex of woodlands making up the remaining fragments of the ancient Bernwood forest, although there are also good isolated colonies scattered elsewhere, including the Warburg Reserve and on the border with Hampshire. This declining situation is reflected nationally and its status is considered to be seriously threatened as remaining major woodland blocks become increasingly fragmented. As its habitats occur in mature woodland, it is very difficult to create conditions that benefit this species in the short term.

Although this butterfly is probably under-recorded due to its elusive behaviour, there is keen interest in studying it and it is unlikely that many of its colonies have been overlooked. It is also possible that some sightings recorded as purple emperors may be optimistic mis-identifications of white admirals and it may be even more scarce than the map shows. It has diminished in abundance in this area and its best hope of survival lies in the sympathetic treatment of these last great forest refuges.

RED ADMIRAL *Vanessa atalanta*

JAN	FEB	MAR	APR	MAY	JUNE	JULY	AUG	SEPT	OCT	NOV	DEC	Flight season

MOST PEOPLE will recognise the name red admiral as a butterfly species, but not all will correctly identify it. The name tends to be attached wrongly to other reddish-coloured members of this family that frequent the garden. As with the white admiral, the name is commonly thought to be a corruption of the older 'red admirable'. This may be a misunderstanding, however, as older texts refer to the name 'admiral' as such, for species with a splash of colour in the middle of the wings – perhaps reflecting the use of colour on naval ensigns to designate the admiral's ship.

The combination of the deep black colour with a scarlet-red stripe across the forewing and the outer margin of the hindwing with white patches towards the tip of the forewing makes this a very distinctive species. Male and female are very similar. The undersides of the forewing are also vivid black, white and red, with a touch of blue, but they can be drawn in behind the mottled brown hindwings to provide camouflage.

Red admiral caterpillar
feeding within a leaf shelter

Red admirals are very unsuccessful at hibernating in this country, but for reasons that are ill understood. They do overwinter successfully in central Europe where winter temperatures are normally cold. Perhaps the average British winter is not consistently cold enough to keep them in deep hibernation and they deplete their fat reserves too quickly. Fortunately, this butterfly is a long-distance wanderer and the few that do survive our winter are supplemented by large numbers of immigrants from the continent, which reach Britain in early spring. These breed here and establish a summer population. The butterfly is found flying late into autumn and is often one of the last species to be seen flying each year. There is a partial return migration south each year, sometimes seen from cross-channel boats, but almost certainly many perish in this country.

The red admiral is one of several nettle-feeding species in the Nymphalidae family. Eggs are laid singly near the edge of the leaf, often on rather isolated straggly plants. The eggs are green and round in shape with fins running out radially from the top. The caterpillar feeds within a purse-shaped shelter which it forms by sticking the leaf edges together with silk to form a pocket. It then feeds from the outer end. The caterpillar varies from black to a grey-green colour with some yellow markings. It also pupates within a leaf shelter, forming a grey pupa flecked with gold marks. Despite its secretive habits, it is not difficult to locate if you can find the tell-tale leaf-shelter. The adult emerges some two weeks later.

As the map shows, this is a very widespread butterfly and it is found almost anywhere where there are either nettles or suitable nectar sources. Bare patches on the map are almost certainly due to lack of recording at the right time rather than absence. It is normally seen in ones and twos; it is seen only in occasional good years in large numbers. It is particularly fond of nectaring on buddleia in summer; in autumn, it favours ivy flowers in hedgerows and on walls and it also drinks the fermenting juices of rotting fruit in the garden, where it will

70

often spend many hours on a sunny day. This intensive feeding builds up the fat reserves it needs to fly south for the winter and for hibernation.

Provided that nettles and availability of nectar sources remain commonplace in our landscape, and suitable conditions also remain widespread on the continent, this butterfly seems to be at little risk and should remain popular.

PAINTED LADY *Cynthia cardui*

JAN	FEB	MAR	APR	MAY	JUNE	JULY	AUG	SEPT	OCT	NOV	DEC

Flight season

T HE PAINTED LADY is an annual immigrant to this country and is another long-distance traveller. It spreads north into Europe each year from north Africa/Arabia, reaching northern Scotland in good years. The numbers that arrive here vary considerably from year to year and probably depend on prevailing wind and weather conditions.

Although it has some resemblance to the red admiral, it is very easy to distinguish, with its rather pale orange markings and white-marked black wing tips. The undersides of the forewings are also boldly marked in the same colours, but the hindwing has a mottled buff appearance with a row of small eyespots to provide camouflage while at rest.

Local arrivals will lay eggs singly on the foodplant, thistles, thus providing a stock of locally reared adults later in the summer. The caterpillars are black and spiny, like those of the others in the vanessid group, and feed inside a tent of leaves. Painted ladies cannot survive our winter – they have no hibernation stage in their life-cycle and those that do not return south will die.

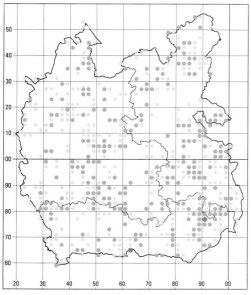

The species features well in gardens – it is particularly attracted to the flowers of buddleia and will spend long periods nectaring there.

The painted lady is widespread over this area, with no particular pattern. It flies far and wide and there is little shortage of thistles on farmland. The number seen each year varies widely, recorded in only 10% of squares in 1987, in 43% in 1988 (when there was a large and noticeable influx in early May) and in 14–16% over 1989 to 1992.

For the survival of this species we are dependent more on it successfully breeding in its north African home than on conditions in this country.

SMALL TORTOISESHELL *Aglais urticae*

Flight season

JAN	FEB	MAR	APR	MAY	JUNE	JULY	AUG	SEPT	OCT	NOV	DEC

THE SMALL TORTOISESHELL is one of the most widely occurring species in this area, and was recorded in about 90% of the squares visited over the atlas survey period. The markings on its wings are quite distinctive and could be confused only with those of the very rare (and possibly extinct) large tortoiseshell. The small white patches near the apex of the forewings and the extended dark area on the hindwings clearly differentiate the small tortoiseshell. Males and females are very similar.

The species is double-brooded and hibernates as an immature adult. It is often seen in mid-winter, flying inside cool buildings, such as outhouses, churches and village halls, whenever there is a sufficiently mild and sunny day to arouse it from its hibernation in a cool corner.

It emerges properly from hibernation in spring, mature and ready to mate. Eggs are laid in large untidy clusters on the undersides of nettle leaves. As many as 100–200 eggs may be laid in one batch. The female chooses a low fresh growth of nettle often at the edge of a larger patch, but in full sun. The eggs are laid within an hour of midday. The female butterfly balances on the edge of the leaf, with her abdomen curled round underneath as she lays. Sometimes a second female may come and lay eggs right next to the first cluster – there is obviously either something special about the location of ideal plants, or else the butterflies instinctively group together when egg-laying.

The caterpillars emerge and feed together in a large gang, on a rough silk tent around the top of the plant. They strip almost all the growth from the top of the plant before moving on to another. The caterpillars are a black and yellow mixture, giving them a greenish appearance, and have branched spines along their backs. They have defensive strategies that rely on numbers. If a feeding 'gang' senses a predator, they will arch their backs and beat in unison, giving the impression of a single, much larger entity, in an attempt to frighten off the attack.

Typical feeding pattern of small tortoiseshell caterpillars

The small tortoiseshell is subject to attack by parasitic tachinid flies that lay inside the body of the caterpillar, and the developing grubs kill their host.

When the caterpillars are larger, they disperse to complete their growth and pupate individually. They hang up in the 'J' shape characteristic of the species in this family, suspended from a silk pad spun onto a twig or stem. The pupa is generally grey-brown, but there is often considerable variation in colour. The adult emerges about 10–14 days later. The summer brood of adults emerge fully mature and will mate almost immediately. Mating occurs deep inside vegetation and is seldom seen. The resulting second brood emerges in late summer to provide the immature adult stock for the following season. There is quite a stagger in the development and the summer and autumn brood adults can appear to fly almost continuously from mid-June through to late September.

To prepare for successful hibernation, the adults must build up good fat reserves during long and intensive feeding in late summer and early autumn. They are very common butterflies in the garden and are particularly attracted to flowers of Michaelmas daisy, ice plant (*Sedum spectabile*) and buddleia. Often, more than 20 adults can be seen nectaring on a single buddleia bush.

Books and articles on butterfly gardening often suggest to gardeners that they keep a nettle patch for butterflies. However, most nettle patches in gardens are in shady corners where they are not easily seen. Small tortoiseshells will only use the fresh growth of nettles where they are in full sun – probably in the centre position in most gardens, which is where most people least want nettles.

This butterfly has probably increased in its abundance over the last few decades. Nettles thrive on soils with excess nitrogen, and will grow well in the many areas where there is fertiliser run-off on farms or on old slurry pits. This species is likely to be with us in good numbers for a long time to come!

LARGE TORTOISEHELL *Nymphalis polychloros*

Flight season	JAN	FEB	MAR	APR	MAY	JUNE	JULY	AUG	SEPT	OCT	NOV	DEC

THE LARGE TORTOISESHELL, principally a woodland butterfly, has become a rare species in recent years. Over the survey period, there were only two reports of large tortoiseshell (both in May). Occasional unconfirmed reports may be mis-identifications of small tortoiseshell (there are clear cases of this in garden survey returns from inexperienced recorders). Confirmed sightings may perhaps be escapes/releases from captive-bred stock. No colonies of this species are known in this country now, and it is generally accepted that it is probably extinct in the wild. The photograph shown here was in fact taken at a butterfly farm, at which this and other rare species are still bred in captivity, and it is a sad reflection that this is the most likely place to see the large tortoiseshell now.

The species uses elm as its foodplant and its increasing scarcity over the last few decades can only have been accelerated by the ravages of Dutch elm disease. It is known from past records that numbers of large tortoiseshells have varied dramatically over periods of time from great abundance to great scarcity.

The large tortoiseshell is closer to the peacock than the small tortoiseshell in that it is single-brooded, with adults emerging in July and August. They overwinter as adults and fly until the end of April the following year. The date strip shows the known British flight season. Large numbers of eggs are laid around small twigs of elm, particularly wych elm, but sometimes willows are used. The caterpillars feed gregariously on a web spun around young leaves and disperse to pupate when fully grown.

The factors explaining these variations and the decline of the species in recent years are not at all understood. This is a very mobile butterfly and while it is possible that it may stage a recovery from the continent, it is also increasingly uncommon there now, which makes the chances of a resurgence in numbers seem remote.

PEACOCK *Inachis io*

JAN	FEB	MAR	APR	MAY	JUNE	JULY	AUG	SEPT	OCT	NOV	DEC

Flight season

THE PEACOCK butterfly must be one of the easiest species to identify in this country – there is no other at all like it. The dominant feature on the uppersides is the arrangement of very large eyespots (reminiscent of the tail markings of the peacock bird) at the outer corner of each wing, set against a rich reddish-brown background. The butterfly often feeds with its wings partly or fully closed, but occasionally flicks the wings sharply open, suddenly exposing the eyespots; the effect on an approaching predator must be quite startling.

The undersides are very dark brown, almost black, and when it is in flight, the predominant effect is of a large black butterfly. Again, this is a distinctive feature – if someone claims to have seen a large black butterfly, the chances are that it was a peacock.

The peacock provides strong evidence that it can taste sweetness through its feet. If you hold an adult firmly but gently by the wings and touch its feet with a spot of jam or honey on your finger, its proboscis will shoot out automatically and it will start to feed. It almost certainly uses this mechanism to assist in locating nectar on flowers.

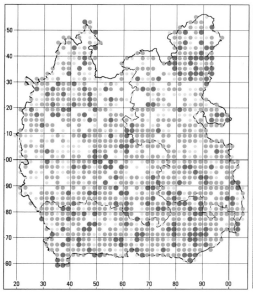

Fully-grown peacock
caterpillar

The life-cycle of the peacock follows a similar pattern to that of the small tortoiseshell, except that it is single-brooded. Eggs are laid at about midday on the undersides of nettle leaves in large and untidy clusters of 200–500. These are often located in the middle of very large patches of nettles, in full sun. The caterpillars are a characteristic deep black colour marked with a peppering of tiny white spots and are armed with rows of spines along the back on each segment. They feed together in large colonies on webs of silk spun round the tops of the plants.

The caterpillars disperse to pupate over quite large distances, often well beyond the boundaries of the nettle patch. The pupa is suspended beneath a twig or leaf and the colour of the pupa is either brown or green to match its surroundings. The adults emerge after about two weeks and have to feed intensively to develop fat reserves for hibernation.

Peacocks choose a variety of dry but cool crevices for hibernation – the dark colouring of the undersides provides excellent concealment. Often they choose to hibernate in cool buildings and may be aroused if the temperature rises. As many as 19 peacocks were seen in a church in Reading on a sunny Saturday one February, as they fluttered against the windows, trying to get out. It is probably best to let them fly out under these conditions – they will find a more suitable place to resume hibernation.

The peacock is a widespread and common species in this area. It occurs in most habitats in the wild and is also a frequent and popular visitor to gardens, where it has a strong preference for buddleia. It seems to be under no threat, given the abundance of nettle patches in our countryside.

COMMA *Polygonia c-album*

Flight season

JAN	FEB	MAR	APR	MAY	JUNE	JULY	AUG	SEPT	OCT	NOV	DEC

Comma nectaring on
buddleia

FROM A DISTANCE, the comma can be confused with a rather ragged fritillary. It has a very irregular margin to its wings, giving it a tattered appearance. The underside is dark and mottled and is marked with the key to the identification of this species, a white comma in the centre of the hindwing. The male is slightly smaller, darker in appearance and a little more ragged than the female. The ragged and dark appearance of the undersides makes a perfect disguise as a dead leaf during hibernation.

Commas are double brooded with timing very similar to that of the small tortoiseshell, flying in spring, mid-summer and again in autumn. Overwintered adults emerge in late spring and lay eggs singly on the edges of nettle leaves. Sometimes eggs are also laid on common hop. The egg is very similar in form to that of the other vanessids, rounded with vertical fins. The newly hatched caterpillar spins a small web below a leaf and feeds from the underside. It progresses later to eating the whole leaf. The fully grown caterpillar is spiny, but is much more boldly coloured with orange and white than its cousins, a colour scheme that breaks up its shape very effectively, even at a short distance. The pupa has an intriguing form that looks like a brown withered leaf from a distance. Close up, it resembles a brown velvet waistcoat with pearl buttons. The adults that emerge early in summer have a much lighter and brighter appearance than the later adults and are known as the form *hutchinsonii*.

Comma caterpillar on nettle

The comma tends to be a species of woodland and mature hedgerow with reasonable cover, rather than open habitats. Unlike the other vanessids, which are fairly gregarious as adults, the comma is rather solitary and quite strongly territorial. The male will often take up a prominent position in a sunny woodland clearing or ride intersection and fly up at anything passing, swooping and gliding around, before returning to the same position. Sometimes it will aggressively buzz the butterfly watcher, even landing on your head or shoulder for a brief time, until you move away again.

This species has undergone a remarkable spread this century, following a very dramatic decline in the 1800s. From a very localised distribution around the mid-Welsh border early this century, it spread to reach most of mid- to southern England by 1940 and has been very common for many years now. There is no good explanation for these dramatic changes in abundance, although it is known that the comma used hop as its main foodplant in the past, at a time when hops were grown on a much more widespread basis. It now predominantly uses nettle, and it may have required a period of adaptation to make the switch from one foodplant to a less preferred choice.

In this area, commas are very widespread and wandering butterflies, although they are seldom seen in more than ones or twos. They have been recorded in over half of the squares visited during the survey, and feature in most garden survey reports. Along with the other vanessid species, they are very fond of buddleia, but also share with red admiral the habit of drinking juices from rotting fruit in autumn, in preparation for hibernation.

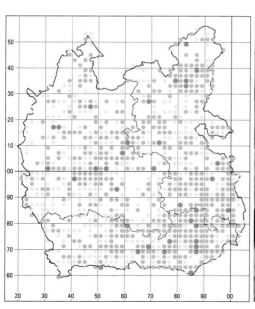

SMALL PEARL-BORDERED FRITILLARY *Boloria selene*

Flight season

JAN	FEB	MAR	APR	MAY	JUNE	JULY	AUG	SEPT	OCT	NOV	DEC

Small pearl-bordered
fritillary upperside

THE SMALL PEARL-BORDERED FRITILLARY is very similar to the pearl-bordered fritillary and requires some experience to distinguish. It is important to realise that both species are physically small compared to the other fritillaries and that the small pearl-bordered fritillary is only slightly smaller than its cousin. The main key differences are to be seen on the undersides. The hindwing of the small pearl-bordered fritillary is darker, with more brown and with a larger number of pearl markings; there are seven pearl markings along the hindwing margin and also seven pearl marks around the cell near the centre of the hindwing with a central black spot. The pearl-bordered fritillary also has seven marginal pearl markings, but has only two around the cell. There are also differences on the uppersides, but distinguishing these in the field is much more difficult.

The butterfly flies in late May and June, when eggs are laid or scattered close to foodplants after the female has located them. The caterpillar differs from that of the pearl-bordered fritillary, in that it has two spines projecting forwards from behind its head, but is otherwise similar, with a black body and two rows of short yellow spines along the back. It feeds on the leaves on the foodplant and hibernates at a partially-grown stage. The fully-grown caterpillar pupates in early spring.

Small pearl-bordered fritillaries require sheltered damp grassland habitats within a woodland structure, containing a good supply of nectar plants and foodplants, the latter being mainly marsh violet or common dog-violet. A typical habitat will be rather wet and muddy underfoot and will have other indicator plants of wet meadow, such as ragged-

Robin and marsh thistle. Areas that have been opened up are preferred and the butterfly is found in both coppiced deciduous woodland and new conifer plantations.

There are now only a few sites on the Berkshire/Hampshire border where colonies of this species are still known, constituting a marked decline since 1975–1984 (see map). Occasional reports are still received from Bernwood, but its status there is not certain now, and some of these may be mis-identified pearl-bordered fritillaries. Widespread drainage of land for agriculture and a reduction in traditional woodland management have dramatically reduced the amount of habitat suitable for this species. It seems unlikely that anything significant can be done to create new habitat, making the maintenance of existing sites a priority. There is a real risk that this species will become extinct in the local area.

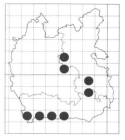

Small pearl-bordered fritillary records, 1975–1984

PEARL-BORDERED FRITILLARY *Boloria euphrosyne*

JAN	FEB	MAR	APR	MAY	JUNE	JULY	AUG	SEPT	OCT	NOV	DEC

Flight season

THE PEARL-BORDERED FRITILLARY is the earliest of the fritillary species to fly each year. It was known in the eighteenth century as the 'April fritillary', whereas the small pearl-bordered fritillary was known as the 'May fritillary'. These old names reflect the 2–3 week difference in their flight periods, and date from before 1752, when the calendar was adjusted by 11 days, effectively 'delaying' the flight seasons into May and June respectively. Of the two species, the pearl-bordered fritillary has a lighter coloration on the uppersides of the wings, but has only two central pearl markings on the hindwing with a generally lighter orange-coloured background. The female is slightly larger than the male.

Mating pearl-bordered fritillaries

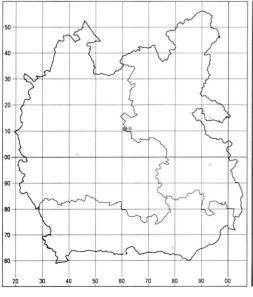

Pearl-bordered fritillary caterpillar

The butterfly flies fast and erratically, with short gliding interludes near to the ground, and can be quite difficult to keep up with. It seems particularly fond of nectaring from the flowers of bugle, which are often found in its habitat, open sunny clearings and wide rides in woodland where the ground cover is sparse.

The female seeks out suitable locations, usually slight hollows which are warmer than fully open positions, where the foodplant, usually common dog-violet, grows. Pale, slightly yellow eggs are laid singly, but not always on the violet leaves; often eggs are laid on other plants near to violets. The caterpillar moves to the edge of a violet leaf to feed. It is black with short yellow spines along its back. It goes into hibernation by autumn when it is partially grown and emerges early the following spring to finish feeding. It pupates suspended from vegetation growing just above the ground.

The distribution of the pearl-bordered fritillary locally has declined dramatically in post-war years. There is one reasonably strong colony left, at Bernwood, but the population there has declined seriously over the past decade. They are also seen just over the border with Hampshire, at Pamber Forest. There have been occasional sightings at a few other locations, but the existence of colonies there has not been confirmed.

The main factor behind this decline is the reduction in availability of suitable habitat. Prime habitat is generated by coppicing in ancient woodland, where newly cleared areas have a flush of rich violet growth on relatively bare ground and a good supply of nectar flowers. Suitable conditions may persist for a few years, but eventually competition from more vigorous herbs and grasses limits the violet growth and results also in loss of the warm bare-soil patches that provide the right microclimate for the growing caterpillars. Unless a cycle of coppicing is sustained, creating new clearings suitable for breeding each year, local colonies become extinct.

Consideration is being given to re-introductions into local ancient woodland sites where the resumption of coppicing has produced apparently suitable conditions, but which are too far distant from known colonies for natural recolonisation to take place. Over the next few years, we should have an opportunity to measure the success of such a scheme. The decline of the pearl-bordered fritillary has reached a point where such re-introduction programmes may be crucial to the survival of the species in this area.

HIGH BROWN FRITILLARY *Argynnis adippe*

Flight season	JAN	FEB	MAR	APR	MAY	JUNE	JULY	AUG	SEPT	OCT	NOV	DEC

HIGH BROWN FRITILLARIES are now believed to be extinct in this area. Although they were once found in many locations across this area, there have been no confirmed sightings since 1980.

The butterfly is large with the bold orange and black chequering characteristic of the fritillaries. When basking, it tends to hold its forewings half concealed behind the hindwings, with the upper edges of the forewings making a semi-circular shape. The undersides of the hindwings are marked with bold pearly-white patches and a row of small white spots surrounded by a reddish brown colour towards the margins. The photographs shown here are not of local specimens – they were taken in north-west England, where there are still some thriving colonies.

High brown fritillary underside

The high brown fritillary is single-brooded and where it still occurs flies between mid-June and August as shown on the flight season strip. Eggs are laid in sunny sheltered positions, often within stands of bracken, on stones or dead vegetation close to the foodplant, mainly common dog-violet. The caterpillar develops within the eggshell, but does not emerge until the following spring. As with other fritillary species, the caterpillars' development requires the local high temperatures that occur in these microhabitats, and they spend long periods of time basking between feeding forays.

The butterfly was formerly found in many larger woodland areas of southern England, but it has declined seriously from these areas and is increasingly confined to sites in the west of England and Wales. At these sites it requires active woodland management, such as coppicing, but it has additional special habitat requirements that limit its viability. The major decline of traditional woodland management practice and subsequent shading of woodland rides and clearings is almost certainly the main factor behind the decline of the high brown fritillary in southern England.

The surviving colonies in western England occur principally on grassland sites, especially on limestone, where the ground vegetation is thin, and partial shelter and strong sunlight combine to produce suitable breeding conditions.

There is no immediate prospect of the high brown fritillary returning to the local area without a major woodland management and reintroduction scheme.

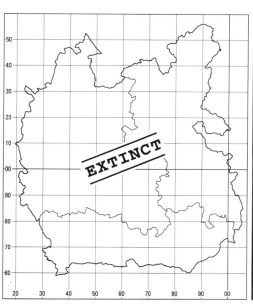

DARK GREEN FRITILLARY *Argynnis aglaja*

Flight season	JAN	FEB	MAR	APR	MAY	JUNE	JULY	AUG	SEPT	OCT	NOV	DEC

Dark green fritillary nectaring on knapweed

WHEN YOU SEE the dark green fritillary in flight, the overwhelming impression is of a vivid orange butterfly with no evidence of dark green. The colouring that gives rise to the name of this species is visible only when the butterfly is resting – there is a partial cover of dull green scales on the undersides of the hind-wings, forming a background to the large pearl-markings. Note also the absence of the red-brown ringed marks inside the margin of the hindwing that distinguish the high brown fritillary.

The female is slightly larger and more darkly marked than the male. Both are very strong and fast flyers over the open grassland habitats that they patrol. On a warm summer day, when they are shooting up and down at breakneck speed close to the ground on a grass slope, they can be very difficult to track down, although they are not known to wander far from the edges of their colony area.

The dark green fritillary's preferred habitats in this area are generally chalk or limestone grassland with comparatively lush vegetation, a good mixture of herbs and a partial cover of scrub giving shelter. The adults are particularly attracted to the large flowers of thistles and knapweeds for nectar.

This species flies in a single brood, from mid- to late June until mid-August. The female lays eggs on violet, preferably hairy violet on chalk grassland habitats, but requires the plants to be in a relatively shaded, cool and humid position, often amongst large tussocks of grass towards the edge of the open grassland. The caterpillar emerges from the egg two to three weeks later and goes directly into hibernation in the leaf litter round the base of

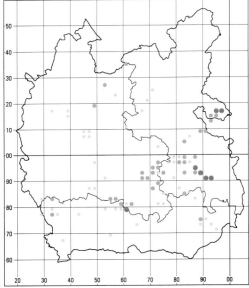

the plant. The following spring, the caterpillars start feeding, eating part of the edge of the leaf and then moving on to another plant. The fully grown caterpillar is black and spiny with red markings along each side.

The dark green fritillary is the most widespread of the fritillary species in this area and in Britain as a whole. However, this species has suffered a significant decline in numbers over the last few years, a pattern repeated over many of the inland regions of the country. This decline is reflected locally in the percentage of recorded squares in which the dark green fritillary was seen each year over the atlas survey period (see page 15).

The long-term decline is probably partly due to a loss of suitable habitat because of extensive scrub invasion on some sites, which reduces the large open areas that this species requires, and a steady increase in rabbit population on other sites, resulting in overgrazing which removes the longer grass and vigorous violet plants.

The recent decline does not seem to be matched by obvious changes in habitat structure over the same period and may be due to short-term factors that are reversible, such as the effects of the recent series of dry summers in reducing the lushness of vegetation.

The map shows that, over the whole of the survey period, there was still a considerable number of colonies, mainly distributed on the chalk grasslands of the Downs and Chilterns and on limestone grasslands elsewhere in the area. There are also some colonies in woodland habitats with large clearings, such as the Warburg Reserve. It is not clear, however, that all of these colonies have survived and the future of the species in this area is uncertain, unless the factors resulting in its recent decline prove to be only temporary.

SILVER-WASHED FRITILLARY *Argynnis paphia*

JAN	FEB	MAR	APR	MAY	JUNE	JULY	AUG	SEPT	OCT	NOV	DEC

Flight season

SILVER-WASHED FRITILLARIES are relatively easy to identify if you manage to get a good view of them. Their name refers to the streaks of silvery-grey that appear like wash-marks across the underside of the hindwing against a rather indistinct green-buff background. The uppersides of the wings are boldly marked with black marks on a bright orange background. The forewings are rather sharply angled at the tips with distinctly concave outer margins, different from the other large fritillaries.

Male silver-washed fritillary

The male is clearly distinguished from the female by the broad black lines of scent scales radiating from the thorax along the upperside of the forewings. These are absent on the female, which has larger black markings and a duller shade of orange, giving an overall darker appearance. A variation of the female, form *valezina*, occurs regularly in southern localities. It has a dusky brown upperside coloration and a pink tinge on the undersides.

The silver-washed fritillary is a species of large mature woodland with a good structure of large clearings and wide ride systems. It is a large butterfly and a fast flyer, but is often attracted to nectar on bramble flowers in the rides.

The adults emerge in early July, and can be seen flying well into August. The females lay their eggs not on the foodplant, but in crevices in the bark of carefully selected mature oak trees which are close to suitable patches of foodplant, usually common dog-violet. The silver-washed fritillary prefers violets growing in rather shaded areas, not in the newly cleared areas used by pearl-bordered fritillaries. The caterpillar emerges about two weeks later and hibernates on the trunk. The following spring it descends to the ground to feed. It is black with thin longitudinal yellow stripes and yellow spines along the back. The two front spines are elongated and extend over the front of the head. The fully grown caterpillar pupates in early June.

The map shows that there are only a few local colonies of this magnificent butterfly left. The main colonies are in Wytham Woods, the Warburg Reserve and on the Hampshire border – Pamber Forest is a particular stronghold and the *valezina* form can also be seen here. Nationally, the main strongholds are in the extensive forests of the south-west, where large and stable colonies still thrive.

Silver-washed fritillaries have disappeared from a number of their former sites in this area over the last decade, as traditional woodland management has declined and many woods have become overshaded and derelict. Plantation woodlands are not generally suitable for this species as they lack the variety of structure needed. Occasional reports are received from some other sites, including Bernwood, but it is unclear whether there is a colony there. It is likely that some isolated reports, particularly from grassland sites, are mis-identifications of the dark green fritillary, which is a much more common species and similar in size.

An introduction of this species was attempted in a wood to the east of Oxford, where, after intensive research and management work, it was believed that conditions had

become suitable. A number of adults from captive-bred stock were released, but weather conditions almost immediately deteriorated. The butterflies disappeared within a few days and subsequent monitoring failed to find any. Another introduction in a wood in Milton Keynes was also unsuccessful in re-establishing a colony. This underlines the difficulties that such projects face and the sad fact that few introductions succeed.

MARSH FRITILLARY *Eurodryas aurinia*

JAN	FEB	MAR	APR	MAY	JUNE	JULY	AUG	SEPT	OCT	NOV	DEC

Flight season

Underside of marsh fritillary

THE MARSH FRITILLARY is quite unlike any of the other fritillary species in this area. Although it has chequered markings on the wings, the arrangement of colour and spots on the wings is quite distinct from the orange with black spots of the other species. The female is distinctly larger than the male, but both are marked on the uppersides with rows of orange and pale spots on a rather brown background. The undersides are much paler and are beautifully marked with a pattern of orange and pale spots.

The scales of the uppersides have a shiny surface, which shows up clearly at some light angles and becomes even more obvious on worn specimens. This is almost certainly what gave rise to the old name of 'greasy fritillary' once used to describe this species.

The butterfly is not found uniquely in marshy habitats, as its name would suggest; nationally, it is found in both damp grassland or marsh conditions and on rather dry heathland or even chalky grassland (as long as there is an abundant supply of its foodplant, devils'-bit scabious, growing vigorously in the right conditions).

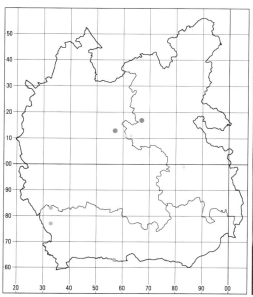

85

Marsh fritillary egg batch
under devils'-bit
scabious leaf

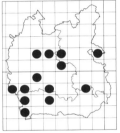

Marsh fritillary records,
1975–1984

Male butterflies emerge in May. By the time the females emerge, several days later, the males are ready and will rapidly locate them and mate. The females are so heavily laden with their egg burden that they can scarcely fly and are constrained to short buzzing flights close to the ground as they search for suitable plants. These are typically large vigorous plants in prominent positions in fairly long grass, with shelter provided by surrounding trees or partial scrub, but with substantial open areas. Eggs are laid in two or three separate layers of about 150 at a time on the underside of a leaf. Further smaller batches may be laid in subsequent days, sometimes on top of previous layings.

The caterpillars exploit their strength in numbers, constructing a large and unsightly web over the plant, where they bask, descending to the leaves to feed. Having demolished one plant, they move on to the next. They hibernate in the same large groups in a silk shelter low in the vegetation and emerge the following spring to recommence feeding to full size. The pupa, formed low in the vegetation, is mainly white, patterned with black dots and marks.

An abundant supply of the foodplant is essential to support such mass feeding, otherwise the caterpillars can literally eat themselves into extinction, exhausting the supply of food before they can complete their development. This has been known to happen when a population explosion has occurred on some sites.

On a European scale, this species has declined to such a serious extent that it has become scheduled as a protected species along with its breeding sites, although this status has not yet been ratified by Britain (it has by Ireland). The British Isles now provide the last major refuge for this species, giving us a special responsibility to conserve remaining colonies. The areas with the largest colonies are south-west Wales, the West Country and several parts of Ireland.

Locally we have lost many sites over the years to land drainage for agricultural and other development. It used to be found in several locations on the Downs and Chilterns (see 10 km square map for 1975–1984). There are colonies left now on Otmoor, in some parts of the complex of fragments of the ancient Bernwood Forest and on the Berkshire/Hampshire border. Small and fragile colonies are also recorded on two sites on the Downs, where the foodplant occurs in a habitat much drier than on the other sites. The numbers seen in all these locations vary from year to year. These remaining colonies are no longer large and we cannot be confident that they will survive. Like many other species, their habitat needs to be managed to control scrub invasion and to make sure that sufficient supplies of the foodplant are available, augmented by additional planting, if necessary.

It is a major challenge for us to live up to our European responsibilities to ensure that those local colonies that remain are conserved. It would be tragic if we were unable to save this attractive butterfly from decline and extinction.

NYMPHALIDAE
THE BROWNS

THE BROWN BUTTERFLY species were formerly classified as a separate family, the Satyridae. Modern taxonomists have now re-classified this group as part of the Nymphalidae, referred to as the sub-family Satyrinae. Like the other 'brush-foots', the brown butterflies have reduced forelegs and use only two pairs of legs for walking.

The butterflies in this sub-family share a number of common features. With only one exception (the marbled white), the species are predominantly brown in coloration, although there is considerable variation on that theme. They all have dilated veins near to the body on the forewings and their antennae are comparatively short. The brown butterfly caterpillars all have grasses as their foodplants, although different species of grass are preferred by different butterfly species. All species overwinter as caterpillars (although some speckled woods overwinter as pupae). The caterpillars vary in colour, but all have a distinctive forked 'tail', which makes them appear to blend into grass stems, rather like a grass flower-head.

All brown species feature eyespots, in the form of black circles with one or more white spots in the centre, on the uppersides and/or the undersides of their wings. Some species have just one pair of eyespots, others have several pairs. It is likely that these eyespots offer significant protection from predatory birds, whose attack is instinctively diverted towards the eyespots and away from the vulnerable body of the butterfly. Damage to the wings merely reduces their flight efficiency and does not affect their physiology or their vital functions.

The brown butterflies inhabit areas with rather long grasses, some in open habitats and others in very sheltered positions. They are not long-distance flyers and have a rather slow and 'floppy' appearance in flight. In this area, some species are highly localised and some are very common, occurring in large numbers where conditions are suitable.

SPECKLED WOOD *Pararge aegeria*

Flight season	JAN	FEB	MAR	APR	MAY	JUNE	JULY	AUG	SEPT	OCT	NOV	DEC

SPECKLED WOODS are very easily recognised, with their pattern of creamy yellow spots on a rich chocolate-brown background. The female tends to be slightly more strongly marked and slightly larger than the male. The undersides have a lighter and more muted pattern of markings, providing camouflage when roosting.

This is a species of shady woodland rides and overgrown hedgerows, characterised by pools of dappled sunlight in otherwise heavily shaded positions, where it is often the only butterfly species to be found. The male typically takes up a perch in the middle of a patch of sunlight. If another enters that patch, he will fly up and challenge the intruder with a contest of spiralling flight. Research, carried out at Wytham Woods some years ago, showed that the male originally occupying the sunny patch will almost always win the contest. Female butterflies entering his territory draw him into a courtship dance, ending in mating at tree-top level.

Smooth white eggs are laid singly on one of a number of grasses, usually on an isolated straggly clump in a sunny position. False brome and cock's-foot are often selected. Eggs are sometimes laid on couch grass, which should make them popular with the gardener! The caterpillar is pale green, with faint yellow stripes running longitudinally, and eats from the edges of the grass leaf. The pupa, usually formed on a grass stem or twig, is pale translucent green.

This species is unusual in Britain in that it has no distinct hibernation stage. It will overwinter as a caterpillar or pupa, depending on which stage of development it has

reached, and will resume activity when the days lengthen and the temperature rises high enough. Adults can be found in flight through most of the year, in a season extending from March through to October, although numbers vary significantly within that time.

The abundance of this species has changed dramatically over the past century. It began to decline in the mid-nineteenth century and its national range contracted dramatically. It reached a low point in the early twentieth century, when it was restricted to only a few parts of the country. Since then, its range and abundance have gradually increased again, to cover most of mid- to southern England and extending into parts of northern Scotland, particularly to the east of Inverness.

Speckled wood caterpillar on a grass blade

In the local area, it is one of the most widespread species, although in any one place it tends to be seen only in small numbers because it is territorial. The typical habitats are plentiful in even small remnants of woodland: woodland edges, rides and footpaths overgrown with scrub. It sometimes comes into gardens, if there is a good shady region near an untidy hedge or rather overgrown area, and it is frequently recorded during garden surveys. Its future seems to be assured.

WALL *Lasiommata megera*

JAN	FEB	MAR	APR	MAY	JUNE	JULY	AUG	SEPT	OCT	NOV	DEC

Flight season

THE WALL BUTTERFLY is well named after its habit of basking on walls, rocks and stony footpaths in full sunshine. The butterfly is boldly marked with deep orange and brown in a pattern that can be mistaken in flight for a rather dark fritillary. A closer inspection shows it to be quite different in the detail of the markings and also in the appearance of its flight. The uppersides are boldly marked with orange spots on a deep brown background. There is an eyespot, sometimes with additional smaller spots, near the apex of the forewing and a series of eyespots parallel to the margin of the hindwing. The male is slightly smaller than the female and has diagonal broad bands of scent scales extending from mid-way along the base of the upper forewing up and out, parallel to the upper wing margin; these are absent in the female. The underside of the forewing is mainly orange, and dominated by the eyespot. The hindwing underside is pale grey-brown, with rather marbled markings and a row of pale eyespots parallel to the outer edge. When the wings are fully closed, the camouflage is excellent against stony backgrounds.

This is a generally widespread butterfly of grassland habitats and it is found particularly where there is sloping and broken ground and shelter, with areas of bare ground or rock to provide basking sites.

The characteristic basking behaviour of this butterfly reflects a need to raise its temperature high enough to fly, breed and lay eggs. In suitable positions, it can raise its temperature to as much as 25 to 30°C, even on a modestly warm day. Locally these habitats

Wall brown egg on a
grass blade

are often found where there are steep embankments, for example along railway lines (used and disused), and soil slippage with extensive bare patches.

The wall is double-brooded, flying first in late April and May and again in July and August. In warm summers, there may be a partial third brood flying in late September and early October. In the hot summers of 1989 and 1990, there was a significant third brood; in 1991, when it was cooler, the summer brood peaked about two weeks later and only a few third brood species were seen, in late October.

The egg is laid on the side of a thin blade of grass. It is smooth, almost spherical and greenish-white in colour. Many grasses are used, including cock's-foot, common bent, Yorkshire-fog, tor-grass and false brome; it is not so much the grass as the local microhabitat that is the key to the butterfly's choice. There is a very strong preference for laying eggs in straggly clumps of grass overhanging bare ground, for example at the top of a small cliff, or at the edges of a pit or hollow. The fully grown caterpillar is a bluish-green colour, with short hairs and a yellow line along each side. The pupa is suspended from a grass stem and is green, turning nearly black as the butterfly forms before emerging.

In the 1970s, wall butterflies seemed to be much more common and were widely found in the gardens and countryside of our area. The butterfly declined rapidly and over the atlas survey period it has been much harder to find. It is now not at all common, except in the north Buckinghamshire/Milton Keynes area, where it is still quite often found in twos and threes. This pattern shows up clearly on the distribution map. It has been suggested that Milton Keynes, a new city known for its widespread landscaping and provision for conservation, provides many of the broken ground habitats the wall requires and that it thrives there. However, it should be noted that it is also common in other parts of north Buckinghamshire well outside of the city development area.

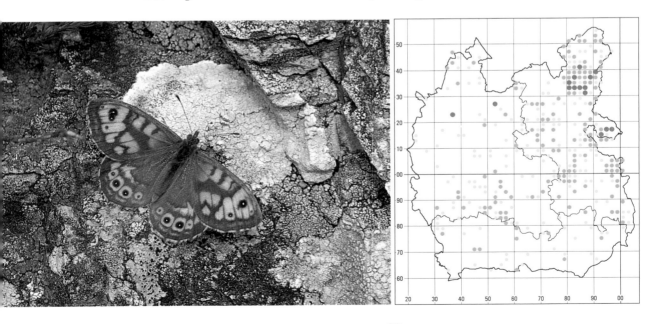

It may be that the wall's need to achieve a high body temperature makes it more prone to variations in long-term weather patterns and that the recent series of rather indifferent summers has affected it adversely. There was an increase in the percentage of squares in which it was seen in 1989 and 1990, but it declined again in 1991 and 1992. Let us hope that populations can recover when warmer weather returns and that we can look forward to seeing more of this species in the future. It would certainly be premature to describe the wall as a threatened species until we know more about the factors governing the variations in its population.

MARBLED WHITE *Melanargia galathea*

JAN	FEB	MAR	APR	MAY	JUNE	JULY	AUG	SEPT	OCT	NOV	DEC

Flight season

THE CREAMY WHITE and deep brown/black markings on the wings of the marbled white make it a very distinctive and attractive butterfly, appropriately described by those who do not know it as a 'black and white butterfly'. Both male and female are marked with a chequered pattern over forewings and hindwings and on the undersides. There are also eyespot markings evident on the undersides, but barely visible on the uppersides. The markings on the male are blacker than those of the female, which are more brown in colour. The background colour varies from brilliant white to a rather yellowish cream. In this country there is no other butterfly like it.

Mating pair of marbled whites – male on the left

The marbled white is a butterfly of wild grassland and occurs in localised, but sometimes very strong, colonies. It likes sizeable areas of grass of medium length; it does not occur

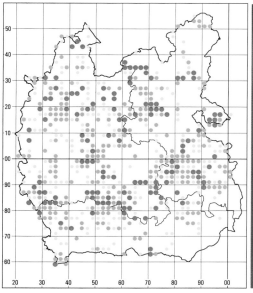

91

Marbled white caterpillar

where there is heavy grazing, for example by rabbits. The butterflies do not normally disperse very far, but occasionally an individual will appear half a mile or more from the nearest colony.

Marbled whites have a habit of basking in the grass, particularly when the weather is cool but bright, or early or late in the day. They will sit with their wings wide open, capturing the heat of the sun, and look rather like white flowers from a distance. On hot sunny days, they are very active flyers, but have a fluttering and rather random flight pattern. They also spend considerable periods of time nectaring, particularly on knapweed and thistle flowers.

The marbled whites' flight season is much more limited than most of the other brown butterflies, lasting from early to mid-June through July, with a few battered individuals surviving a little longer, into late August.

Egg-laying is very difficult to observe. After mating, the female flutters low over the grass and simply scatters eggs in flight as she bobs up and down amongst the vegetation. The egg is spherical and pale white in colour. The caterpillar hatches about three weeks later, eats the shell and goes straight into hibernation amongst the ground litter. It emerges again in early spring and initially feeds during the day. Later stages feed only after dark and can be found relatively easily with a torch and a little patience, as they move up to feed at the top of a grass blade, shortly after dusk in May. The fully grown caterpillar is a light ochre colour with characteristic tails and a brown stripe down the centre of the back. The pupa is a similar pale colour and is formed on or near the soil. The adult emerges about three weeks later.

Although various species of grass, including cock's-foot and sheep's-fescue, are used for feeding, it has been discovered recently that red fescue is an essential requirement for one of the early stages of the caterpillar. This may be one reason why the marbled white is so localised, although studies of the distribution of red fescue would be needed to confirm such a theory.

In this area, the species occurs in numerous localised colonies, some of which number many hundreds and even thousands. These occur widely on open grasslands on the Downs and Chilterns and on limestone in north Oxfordshire, but it also occurs on dry heath grasslands, such as those on sandy beds of the corallian limestone ridge between Oxford and Faringdon. Towards the north, where it is perhaps marginally cooler, marbled whites are found less widely and tend to be even more localised. Many of the colonies in north Buckinghamshire occur on disused railway cuttings, which provide ideal sheltered breeding sites. Several colonies are found on wide roadside verges. Embankments generally provide good conditions; there are marbled white colonies at most of the A34 intersections between the Downs and Oxford.

In this area the marbled white is quite widely distributed, with a good number of strong colonies, and its occurrence correlates well with sites for some of our other rare and localised butterfly species. It seems, therefore, to provide an indication of relatively rich grassland habitat with conservation value.

GRAYLING *Hipparchia semele*

JAN	FEB	MAR	APR	MAY	JUNE	JULY	AUG	SEPT	OCT	NOV	DEC	Flight season

GRAYLINGS are seldom seen in the local area. They are the largest of the brown butterflies and are quite distinctive in their habits. The uppersides of the wings, which can be glimpsed only in flight, are a deep brown with pale patches towards the outer margins of the forewing and hindwing. There are two eyespots on each upperwing, a distinctive feature of this species. These are seen more easily on the underside of the upper wing just after it has landed and can be seen in the photograph of mating graylings used here. The underside of the hindwing is marked with a dark grey-brown pattern of camouflage so effective that, when it lands, it seem to disappear completely from sight.

Like most of the brown butterflies, the female is slightly larger than the male. The female is more brightly marked on the upperside of the forewing than the male, which has dark scent scale bands extending diagonally upwards from the body, similar to those of the wall butterfly, but less distinct.

Graylings are primarily coastal butterflies in this country, commonly occurring near cliffs, rocky foreshores and sand dunes. Inland, it is a species of dry habitats and in this area is now found only on a few remaining fragments of heathland and one downland site.

The grayling flies very strongly and changes direction quickly, making it difficult to follow. When it lands, it closes its wings immediately and they will stay firmly closed (unless it flies off). At first, the forewings are held extended above the hindwings so that one or both of the eyespots are visible. A bird seeing the grayling land would probably strike almost immediately, but at the eyespots, rather than the body. Within a minute or so, the

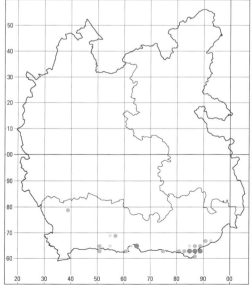

93

forewings are pulled down behind the hindwings, concealing the eyespots and providing perfect camouflage. In bright sunshine, it then turns to face the sun and leans its body over to match the angle of the sunlight. In this position it casts no shadow (adding to its concealment) and also avoids being overheated by the sun. In cool or shady weather, it will turn sideways to the sun to raise its temperature.

Graylings fly in a single brood during July and August. Eggs are laid on grass. It is not known what species are chosen in this area, but elsewhere it is known to lay on sheep's-fescue, which does occur locally. The eggs are white spheres with vertical ribs running around the circumference. They hatch after two to three weeks and the caterpillar feeds on young grass shoots. It hibernates whilst partially developed, in its third stage. The fully grown caterpillar is similar to that of the marbled white, with a light grey-brown colour and longitudinal dark stripes, and also feeds only by night.

Locally, it is confined to the acidic heathlands on the Berkshire/Hampshire border, as shown on the map. It used to occur at several chalk grassland sites on the Downs, but has not been seen at most of these for a decade or more, although it was recorded at one remaining site on the Lambourn Downs during the survey period. Several of the sites where it appears are protected; many are BBONT reserves. Typical sites, such as at Owlsmoor and Sandhurst, have a sandy soil partially covered by heather and peat.

Its status is not assured in these inland habitats and, although it is regularly seen on most of its sites, it is seldom seen in large numbers. The management of its habitat requires that open areas are kept free from scrub and birch invasion, with control of the heather growth, often by burning (controlled and, at times, uncontrolled). This management regime also suits the silver-studded blue, which shares several of the remaining heathland sites on which graylings are found. These areas of southern Berkshire are currently in the green belt, but even so remain under threat from development.

GATEKEEPER *Pyronia tithonus*

Flight season	JAN	FEB	MAR	APR	MAY	JUNE	JULY	AUG	SEPT	OCT	NOV	DEC

Mating gatekeepers – the male is the smaller one

T HE GATEKEEPER is also known as the hedge brown and both names refer to the habitat in which it is usually seen, patrolling along hedgerows and amongst broken scrub. The uppersides of this butterfly are deep brown with a broad flush of deep orange extending over much of the forewing and the central part of the hindwing.

The male is often strikingly smaller than the female and, like other brown males, he has a broad band of scent scales extending from the base, near to the body, up and out to the centre of the forewing. Both male and female are smaller than the meadow brown, the only species with which the gatekeeper is likely to be confused.

The eyespot on the upper corner of the forewing, visible on upper and undersides, is black with two white spots in the centre. In some specimens, there are also one or more eyespots along the margin of the hindwing. The underside of the hindwing is mid-brown tinged with red, with a wash of creamy white across the outer half and marked with four or five white spots.

This common butterfly is a regular inhabitant of hedgerows and roadsides where it may form quite significant colonies. It is often found nectaring on bramble and ragwort flowers in quite large numbers. When it is seen in the garden, it shows a preference for the flowers of marjoram. It will spend much time basking in the sun with its wings held open, often on the leaves of scrub and hedge plants.

Gatekeepers are single-brooded. The adults emerge later than meadow brown adults, generally in early to mid-July, and they fly for a fairly well-defined six weeks. The start of their season varies by about ten days between warm and cool years (see page 14).

Eggs are laid on or scattered around long grasses at the foot of shrubs or hedges. The eggs are white with vertical ribs, but develop 'rusty' brown patches as they mature. The caterpillar feeds on various grasses, including couch, fescues and bents, and hibernates in its second stage. Like the caterpillars of other browns, it is a nocturnal feeder in its later stages. It is grey-brown in colour and slightly hairy with longitudinal stripes and a forked tail. The pupa is formed under a leaf and is striped with white and brown to provide very effective camouflage.

The gatekeeper is a common butterfly in southern England, but is not found in the north or in Scotland. The distribution map shows it to be a very widespread and common species in this area. Any gaps on the map are probably attributable to patchy recording rather than the butterfly's absence, since there are few areas that do not have enough scrub or hedgerow to support a colony. Gatekeepers thrive where fields have a wide uncultivated margin near to a hedge, allowing a variety of wild grasses and

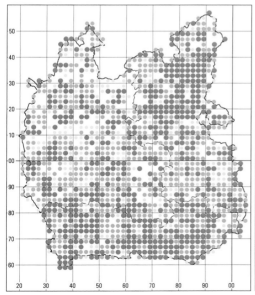

flowers to become established, and their presence in such places indicates at least a threshold level of value for wildlife.

MEADOW BROWN *Maniola jurtina*

Flight season

JAN	FEB	MAR	APR	MAY	JUNE	JULY	AUG	SEPT	OCT	NOV	DEC

Underside of meadow brown

THE MEADOW BROWN is amongst the commonest and most widely recorded species in this area. The adult is relatively large with deep brown uppersides. The female has broad orange patches across the forewings with a bold black eyespot with a white centre; occasional individuals are found with a small second spot within the black mark. The male has little or no orange on the uppersides and the eyespot is generally smaller. He also has a barely visible dark band of scent scales running out diagonally from the base of the forewing towards the centre.

The hindwings are larger than the forewings and have a slightly scalloped edge. The underside of the forewing is mainly orange with a brown margin and the same clear eyespot as on the upperside. The hindwing underside is a dull brown and has a lighter brown irregular band crossing parallel to the outer margin with up to five very small black spots.

Meadow browns are well named after their favoured habitat, open grassland with a good variety of grasses of medium length, mixed with herbs to provide nectar. In unimproved meadows the numbers can be very large, with several individuals per square metre. With every step, two or three will fly up, giving a very dynamic feeling of summer. A group of

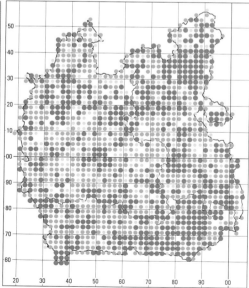

over a hundred seen flying on just a few yards of roadside in west Oxfordshire turned out to be refugees from a field just over the hedge, where hay was being cut.

Meadow browns are by no means confined to open grassland and will appear in woodland rides and clearings, along tracks, roadside verges and the margins of cultivated fields, and in gardens. They are probably the most ubiquitous of our butterflies.

They like to nectar on thistles, knapweeds and brambles, but will also visit many other flowers. They have an erratic fluttering flight close to the ground. In cooler weather, they sit in the grass with their wings spread open to catch the sun, in order to raise their body temperature. Meadow browns are able to fly on relatively cool days, when few other butterfly species are on the wing, and they are generally the first to appear after rain, or even during the rain.

Meadow browns are single-brooded and fly from about the end of May until late August. The earliest individuals emerge from particularly sheltered hollows or slopes where the higher temperature accelerates development. Often there are a few stragglers which linger on into autumn, looking very worn, tattered and pale in colour compared to the newly emerged specimens earlier in the season.

Meadow browns are quite often seen mating in the grass or in adjacent shrubs. The female lays eggs in an apparently careless fashion, fluttering low over the grasses, sometimes laying on a grass blade and sometimes just dropping eggs in flight. There is little need to be particular, as foodplants are abundant. The favoured plants are fine grasses, including meadow-grasses, bents and the finer rye-grasses. The eggs are particularly small in comparison with other butterfly eggs, being only about 0.5 mm in diameter, and are creamy with rusty blotches.

The young caterpillar eats during the day. It does not enter true hibernation, but simply stops feeding and retreats into the undergrowth when the weather is too cold, emerging again briefly during mild days. The following year, the larger caterpillar becomes nocturnal. Fully grown caterpillars are green with short hairs, a thin yellow stripe along each side and a dark green stripe down the back. They have the forked 'tail' typical of the browns.

The pupa is formed suspended from a stem. It is bright green with black linear markings, which break up its shape amongst the grass shadows. Darker forms also occur, when it is close to the ground amongst dead vegetation. The adult emerges between ten days and a month later, depending mainly on local temperature.

The local distribution map is almost completely covered for this species – it was seen in over 95% of the squares visited during the survey. In the handful of squares where it was not recorded, that was almost certainly because these squares were not surveyed in midsummer. The strongest colonies occur on the main grassland areas, on the chalk of the Downs and Chilterns, the heaths of east Berkshire and on the limestones of north Buckinghamshire and Oxfordshire. This butterfly seems not to be under any threat, provided that there are at least remnants of grassland left. If major gaps in its distribution do appear in the future, then that would indicate a very serious degradation in the quality of our countryside for wildlife.

RINGLET *Aphantopus hyperantus*

Flight season	JAN	FEB	MAR	APR	MAY	JUNE	JULY	AUG	SEPT	OCT	NOV	DEC

Mating ringlets

T HE RINGLET is a delightful chocolate-brown coloured butterfly which can, with practice, be recognised in flight. The uppersides range from a very deep, almost black shade of brown on the male to a slightly paler shade on the female. Both become paler as scales are worn off. The wings are fringed with white, making a bold contrast with the dark colour. There are two or three eyespots faintly visible on the uppersides of the forewing and hindwing. The undersides of the wings are a paler brown colour, clearly marked with striking black spots with white centres, ringed with yellow. Viewed at close quarters, the undersides cannot be mistaken for another species.

The ringlet is a butterfly of damp and often shaded grasslands, and frequents woodland rides, clearings and edges, as well as open areas with very long grass, typically knee-deep, where it can occur in strong colonies. It has an erratic flight, bobbing up and down in a quite characteristic pattern. It will fly in very poor conditions when almost no other butterfly is in flight. In cool overcast conditions, it will sit in hollows deep in the grass and bask with its wings open to catch any warmth that it can. It often chooses bramble and thistles for nectaring, rather than smaller flowers.

Ringlets are single-brooded, flying later than meadow browns, from mid-June through to early August, with a few late stragglers extending to the end of August.

Glossy cream-coloured eggs, with an upside-down bowl shape, are dropped from flight as the female bobs low over the grass. The caterpillars are known to feed on dense tussocks of cock's-foot and false brome grasses. They hibernate at their second stage. The larger

98

stages of the caterpillar are nocturnal and can be found with a torch after dusk in May. They are a grey-brown colour and hairy with longitudinal stripes and twin 'tails'. The pupa is similar in colour, with black stripes, and is formed near the ground in a grass tussock.

This species is widely distributed and common in most areas where its habitat occurs. There are gaps in its local distribution over the larger urban areas, such as Reading and Slough, where suitable habitat is in short supply. There was just one 10 km square, TQ07, in which it was not recorded within Berkshire/Buckinghamshire – the area west of the M25 and north of Staines, not an obvious area for good butterfly habitat. Elsewhere, its distribution extends over large woodland areas and shaded corners. On the drier Downs, it tends to be confined to small areas where there is greater shade, such as wide field margins or damp corners with a well-developed uncut hedge or at least partial tree cover.

SMALL HEATH *Coenonympha pamphilus*

JAN	FEB	MAR	APR	MAY	JUNE	JULY	AUG	SEPT	OCT	NOV	DEC	Flight season

THE SMALL HEATH is the smallest of our brown butterflies and, although rather inconspicuous, it is well worth a closer look. The butterfly always keeps its wings closed when at rest, so the orange-brown uppersides of the wings are visible only in flight. The undersides of the forewings are also orange-brown, with grey margins and a small neat white-on-black eyespot towards the top corner. The undersides of the hindwings are grey, dark towards the body and lighter towards the margin, with a slight creamy smudge separating these shades in the upper half.

99

The small heath is found in a variety of open wild grassland habitats, usually in dry conditions where the turf is short, grazed by sheep or rabbits. It is found on heathland, after which it is named, but is also common on chalk and limestone grasslands.

Males are fiercely territorial and will sit on a perch to challenge intruders. They will engage in extended dogfights with other males, often lasting for longer than the patience of the butterfly watcher. They fly together in a tight spiral, hardly moving vertically or any distance over the ground, until eventually one of them (usually the smaller) breaks off and flies away. When not resting or seeking a mate, they will nectar from short flowers close to the ground, such as smaller thistles and members of the daisy family. On landing, the forewings are extended slightly to show the eyespot, but are often withdrawn behind the hindwings after a few minutes to aid camouflage, in a similar way to the grayling.

There seem to be two or, in a warm summer, possibly three broods of small heath each year, with the main abundance from early May to late June and from mid-July into late August. Locally, the broods overlap significantly in mid-summer in most years, making it hard to distinguish broods clearly. They will fly in a variety of weather conditions and can be seen even on rather cool and windy days.

Eggs, which have vertical ribs, are laid singly on blades of fine grasses, including sheep's-fescue and meadow-grasses. The first eggs a female lays are green, but those laid later in her life are yellow. The caterpillars are green with longitudinal stripes and feed on young grass shoots; they overwinter at different stages, depending on their development when the weather becomes cold. Not all first brood caterpillars become adults in the same year – some enter hibernation at that stage. In general, the more developed the caterpillars are before winter, the sooner they pupate and emerge as adults the following spring. The pupa, formed hanging from a plant stem, is green with black streaks.

Nationally, the small heath is one of our most widely distributed species, not just in latitude, but also in altitude – it is recorded from sea level up to about 750 m. The local distribution of the butterfly is fairly widespread, but the best concentrations are on the Downs and Chilterns, the limestone grasslands of north Buckinghamshire and north Oxfordshire and amongst the heaths of south and east Berkshire. There are also many colonies on the residues of sandy heathlands on the low corallian limestone ridge between Oxford and Faringdon; the low-fertility soils of worked-out sand pits provide ideal conditions for large colonies, for example in the Cothill area, where there are several BBONT reserves. Although there are only relatively minor variations in overall abundance from year to year, major changes become apparent locally if the butterflies' favoured short dry grassland habitats are lost to development.

SIGHTINGS OF UNUSUAL VAGRANT SPECIES

During the period of the atlas survey, a few unusual species which are not normally found in this country were seen. It is sometimes possible to see the occasional continental European species well out of its normal range – in the past, there have been random reports of, for example, Camberwell beauty and Queen of Spain fritillaries in this area. These days, odd specimens of unusual butterflies are often more likely to have escaped from one of the many butterfly houses now breeding exotic species in this country (for example, a Gulf fritillary was seen wandering in Blenheim Park some years ago when there was a butterfly house there) or to be releases (accidental and occasionally deliberate) from captive-bred stock reared by amateurs.

Such individual sightings of vagrant species are interesting to record, but have little conservation significance. However, if longer-term climate changes, perhaps resulting from the 'greenhouse efect', were to raise the average temperature significantly or alter our weather pattern from the usual warm, changeable summers and damp, mild winters to greater extremes of hot and cold, then continental species may be able to colonise Britain over a widespread area.

The following sightings were documented in Berkshire, Buckinghamshire and Oxfordshire between 1987 and 1993.

LONG-TAILED BLUE *Lampides boeticus*

A single long-tailed blue was seen, clearly identified and described in the large rural garden of a house in Beaconsfield on 23 May 1989. It spent over half an hour there, giving ample opportunity for the recorder to identify it and to show it to others. It is very unusual to see this species in Britain and it cannot survive our winters.

The long-tailed blue tends to have a faster, more darting flight than our native blues and is easy to identify with its pattern of brown and white wavy lines across the underwings. There are small eyespots on the hindwings next to the tails. The green caterpillar, similar in shape to that of the other blues, is sometimes found in consignments of fresh legumes, such as mange-tout peas, imported from other European countries. Indeed, one such caterpillar was reared to maturity and provided the finder with a rewarding sight of an adult. It uses various pod-bearing plants of this family as foodplants and was once known, appropriately, as the 'pea-pod blue'. A small colony was also found on a site in London in 1990, although its origin has not been identified.

TIGER SWALLOWTAIL *Papilio turnus*

Swallowtail butterflies were mysteriously reported from the Cholsey area in the summer of 1989, although none of the reports were detailed enough to allow the species to be confirmed. In July 1990, a local recorder photographed a "swallowtail" nectaring on buddleia in a garden in Moulsford. From the photograph, sent to the author, it was possible to identify it as an American species, the tiger swallowtail, similar to, but distinct from, the British swallowtail. As it is extremely unlikely that it could have reached this country naturally, it could only be assumed that this, along with the other "swallowtails" seen the previous year, were releases from captive stock. It has since been established that a local amateur breeder was in the habit (an illegal act now, of course) of releasing a few males from bred stock, an activity which he regarded as harmless.

The British swallowtail, *Papilio machaon*, was once a fairly widespread species in England and may have occurred in this local area long ago, at a time when there was extensive fenland and marshes, before the advent of agricultural drainage schemes. It is now virtually confined to the Norfolk Broads, where it has a reasonably stable stronghold, but it remains dependent on preservation of its very wet habitat.

EUROPEAN MAP *Araschnia levana*

Considerable local interest was aroused by confirmed sightings of the European map butterfly in a particular part of the local area in 1992 and 1993. Both first and second brood specimens were seen each year on private land, in the same general area, and there was speculation that it might be breeding successfully.

This butterfly has spread fairly widely in recent years across the middle part of continental Europe, extending across northern France in a very broad band well into Russia. The map butterfly is a medium-sized species related to the vanessids. It is particularly unusual among European species in that the spring and summer broods are quite different in appearance. The spring brood of adults, which were seen flying in this area in May, are a reddish orange colour, reminiscent of a small comma, whereas the summer brood, which were seen flying locally in August, are dark-brown, almost black, not unlike a small white admiral with which it shares a tendency to glide in flight. Eggs are laid in strings, hanging from the foodplant, nettle, on which the caterpillars feed gregariously.

Although the origin of this 'colony' was unknown at first, it was discovered by chance in late 1993 that the sightings were the result of deliberate releases of live specimens from captive bred stock, being carried out quite unofficially and illegally by an individual breeder. Since releases were allegedly made repeatedly, it is not possible to draw any firm conclusions from the timing or extent of these sightings. The map's requirements are not well understood and it is not known why it cannot colonise this country naturally.

PREDATORS
AND PARASITES

BUTTERFLIES form part of a complex food chain involving many other species and, like other species, they are subject to predators, parasites and diseases that influence their survival.

Peacock with missing eyespot after bird attack

Consider what would happen without predators or disease. If we assume for simplicity that a typical female butterfly, if uninterrupted, will lay an average of perhaps 200 eggs. Each egg has the potential to lead to a mature adult insect, either male or female. Let us assume that equal numbers of males and females develop. In each generation, then, each female will produce 100 females in the next generation, and each of these, if fertilised, will produce 100 in the following generation – that is 10,000 after only two generations, and one million after three! The result would be a population explosion.

In a stable population with roughly equal numbers in each generation, on average only about one egg in a hundred will lead to a fertile female laying in the next generation. In other words, the mortality rate is about 99% for this simplified example. This mortality rate is brought about as the result of diseases, and attacks by predators and parasites.

Of the larger predators, birds dominate the predation of adult butterflies. In mid-summer, when a large hatch of peacock butterflies can result in 30–50 adults nectaring on the buddleia, flycatchers and even birds such as sparrows will take quite a number, leaving only the tell-tale signs of discarded butterfly wings scattered on the ground.

Butterflies have evolved various mechanisms to reduce the effectiveness of bird attack. The erratic zig-zagging flight of many species makes them very difficult to follow, let alone catch on the wing. Some have developed eyespots on their wings, a feature which is most strongly expressed in the peacock. This butterfly uses the trick of sitting with its wings partly closed and occasionally flicking them open, revealing a flashing set of eyes, which is likely to startle any approaching bird.

The eyespots also act to divert the instinctive strike by the bird from the vulnerable body of the insect to the outer parts of the wing where damage is less critical. The photograph shows the effects of a bird attack on a peacock butterfly, diverted to one of the very vivid eyespots. This butterfly has slightly impaired flight but its vital functions are not otherwise affected and it can still feed and breed.

Birds also eat insect larvae and pupae. In winter especially, smaller birds rely for food on the larvae and pupae of various insects and will hunt vigorously through the undergrowth seeking them out. A hard cold winter with thick snow on the ground provides effective protection for the insects, which are well capable of withstanding low temperatures, whereas small birds risk starvation. In contrast, a mild damp winter also favours microscopic

103

Crab spider preying on
meadow brown

Red mites parasitising
large skipper

Parasite cocoons on
white admiral caterpillar

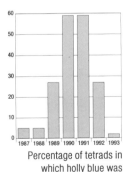

Percentage of tetrads in
which holly blue was
recorded, 1987–1993

'predators' of butterflies – bacterial infection and mould growth add a further mortality factor which can also affect the eggs.

Spiders are perhaps the most notorious of the predators on insects. The body of a butterfly caught in a sticky web provides a sizeable meal and it is soon trussed up by the attendant spider. Crab spiders have evolved coloration to match the flowers and plants on which they conceal themselves to await the arrival of food. For example, bright yellow crab spiders can be found hidden underneath a buttercup. They will pounce on a butterfly alighting there for nectar, bite into its body injecting a paralysing toxin and then carry it nearer to ground level. There the spider will consume the contents of the body of the butterfly, leaving only the shrivelled skin and the wings.

Red spider mites are parasites of some species. They are sometimes seen, for example, on large skippers and meadow browns. They attach themselves to the thorax, as many as six or seven at a time, and live off the body fluid of their host. This debilitates and slows down the butterfly, not actually killing it, but making it unable to breed successfully.

Attack by parasites can lead to an interesting interdependence of one species on another. Some parasites are specific to a particular host species, and are therefore dependent on having an adequate population of the host to provide for their own survival. If the parasite is too 'successful', the next generation of butterflies is seriously depleted and the parasite population in turn suffers high losses.

Holly blues have a parasite believed to be host-specific, an Ichneumonoid wasp, *Listrodomus nycthemerus*. This wasp injects an egg into the body of a holly blue caterpillar. The egg hatches and the wasp larva develops rapidly once the host caterpillar pupates, eating the entire contents of the pupal case, which it then uses as a cocoon for its own pupation. The developed adult wasp then emerges from the pupal case (see photo on page 60). There is a theory that the swings in the size of holly blue populations are caused, at least in part, by the changes in the success of predation by this wasp.

Other parasites, such as *Apanteles sibyllarum*, a tiny wasp species that attacks white admirals, lay several eggs inside the caterpillar. The grubs hatch and feed on the internal body fluids of the caterpillar, making it very listless and slow. The grubs grow rapidly and when mature, bore their way out of the caterpillar's skin and form little cocoons on the outside of its body. The caterpillar is left wasted and does not survive. A similar species, *A. glomeratus*, attacks large white caterpillars, causing heavy losses. Many tens of tell-tale yellow cocoons can be seen 'decorating' the shrivelled bodies of the caterpillars, after they have crawled up a wall to locate a site for pupation. This wasp is probably the main natural control limiting the population of this pest.

This interdependence of species means that simple attempts at pest control often lead to unexpected effects as natural predators are also removed and another species may expand to unusual numbers. Great care has to be taken when we try to control insect populations.

MANAGING HABITATS TO CONSERVE BUTTERFLIES

MANY OF OUR COMMON BUTTERFLIES are capable of adapting to changes in the local countryside. This is reflected in their broad distributions over the three counties. There are, however, several species with much more specialised requirements. As a result, their distributions are more limited and remaining colonies are dwindling and threatened with extinction. It is the conservation of their specialised habitats that is the key to retaining these threatened species in our countryside.

Even the butterflies that we think of as 'common' face long-term threats. Many survive on small remnants of wild countryside or very localised areas of roadside verge or hedgerow. They remain common only as long as such fragments of habitat remain widespread. Because of constant changes in the countryside, many such habitats are ephemeral. Small and fragile colonies may be there one year, but gone the next. If another location nearby becomes suitable, then they may move in and colonise it. These local re-colonisations keep the common species going, provided that suitable locations remain in sufficient proximity to one another. If we take these species for granted and allow further major losses of the wild corners in our developed countryside, then we risk the permanent loss of many colonies of relatively common butterflies.

Habitats and the landscape

At one time, the three counties, like the rest of the country and the rest of Europe, had a truly natural landscape. After the last ice age and the retreat of the glaciers to Arctic regions, the countryside was mainly covered in forest. Forest, in this case, means a natural succession of native and predominantly broad-leaved trees – oak, ash and maple, for example. There are only three conifers native to this country, Scots pine, juniper and yew; modern forestry plantations are dominated by imported trees, such as spruce and firs.

The forests were inhabited by a rich mixture of flora and fauna, with many larger mammals – bears, wild boar and wolves, as well as deer, badgers, foxes and many rodents. Trees grew from seedlings to full maturity, cleared only by major storms, by fires started by lightning strikes, or even by beavers. The temporarily open areas had a succession of herbs and grasses which thrived until seedling trees grew and shaded over the ground. The herb seeds lay dormant in the soil until the next accidental clearing led to conditions suitable for germination. This was the legendary 'wildwood', long gone now, apart from the merest indications in eastern Europe.

The natural cycle of the wildwood forest lasted until man began to make an impact with organised development. Man was originally a hunter-gatherer, in balance with the natural landscape. Early agriculture was on a small scale. Clearings within the forest were probably used to form plots for cultivation. With agriculture came more permanent settlements, which gradually expanded. By the Iron Age, settlements existed in most parts of the country and had transformed a large fraction of the natural forest.

Recent archaeological evidence indicates that forest was cleared from the Downs about 5,000 years ago as part of the development of agriculture. By about 1000 BC, extensive clearances in our region would already have formed a landscape similar to that of today.

The Roman invasion of Britain brought the innovations of a 'civilised' society. They built roads across the country to provide supply routes and rapid troop deployment. They developed large towns based on new trading systems. Most of these ancient Roman routes and towns remain to this day – evidence of their impact on our country. The intensity of agriculture was increased to supply these new communities.

After the fall of the Roman empire agriculture declined. Successive invasions from the continent brought their own contributions to our society – Saxons, Danes and then the Norman invasion and feudalism. The growth of villages and towns called for more agriculture and more timber for building and fuel. Much local woodland has been under human management since that time, mainly as coppice harvested for material to support this growth. The Normans introduced rabbits into this country as a valuable delicacy. Wild colonies became established and populations grew as larger mammal predators retreated with the declining forests. The price of rabbits, of course, dropped.

The Black Death brought devastation in the fourteenth century and much agricultural land was left derelict or reverted to grazing until the human population recovered.

As Britain developed into a single kingdom, it grew in economic, political and military strength. The defence of the island required a strong navy and sailing ships required very large quantities of timber – forests were exploited on an ever larger scale.

The growth of the wool trade and the immense profits to be made by the wool merchants increased demand for open grassland to support larger numbers of sheep. Many of the old towns of the Cotswolds bear witness to the wealth of this successful industry. As trading grew, a transport infrastructure was developed, firstly by a flurry of canal-building in the late 1700s and early 1800s, until the new railways began to make an impact across the countryside. The wider distribution of wealth led to accelerating economic expansion. Improving health meant that more people survived and the population grew.

The industrial revolution not only created employment, transportation and expanding cities, but began to revolutionise agriculture. As we entered the twentieth century, man was everywhere showing that civilisation had the means to control nature. The impact of the second World War, in particular, brought the realisation that we needed to be more self-sufficient as a nation and farmers were given every encouragement and incentive to increase production. The clear objective was to feed our people. Farmers responded magnificently and, linked with the benefits of technological development, intensive farming resulted in that objective being met. But there was a cost to pay. The greater use of large machinery and maximum use of the land area to improve efficiency led directly to the loss of hedgerows as fields grew in size. More and more marginal land was brought into cultivation. Much of the ancient grassland of the Downs was ploughed up for cereal farming and many remnants of woodland were removed.

We are now part of a wider European Community and subject to the notorious Common Agricultural Policy. This strives to manage an overproduction of food within Europe while seeking to maintain the economic standards of farmers. The brakes had to be applied to prevent a catastrophic collapse of the farming system. Quotas were introduced for basic food production, with incentives to diversify into other crops – oil-seed rape and linseed have become commonplace in our landscape over the last decade – and farming is no longer seen as a good business prospect. The downturn has strongly affected the economically marginal areas of agriculture – hill-farming and sheep rearing are now in dramatic decline. Locally, the result is a significant reduction in traditional sheep grazing on those parts of the Downs not already ploughed. Where grazing is removed, the grass length increases and scrub begins to invade. The introduction of myxomatosis in the 1950s, in an attempt to control an over-population of rabbits, also contributed to the reduction in grazing.

Woodland management went into steep decline after the last World War. There was no longer the demand, in the age of new materials, for timber products from our ancient forests. Forestry plantations, with fast-growing imported coniferous species, designed for large scale harvesting, supplanted the traditional methods of coppicing and hardwood timber cultivation. As a result, many woodlands have become over-grown and derelict. Some are now managed for game shooting; where this is done with care, conservation needs can be met as well, but in too many cases, the wrong strategies are used without benefit.

As Britain's economy prospered and car ownership became widespread, demand for roads steadily increased. Firstly, major roads between towns and cities were improved for fast motor vehicles. Then increasing urban congestion led to the development of by-passes and motorways to take long-distance traffic away from the cities. This increased the incentive for more people to travel by road and reduced the costs of road haulage, at the expense of the railways. As road capacity increases, demand increases and more and more motorways with more and more lanes are built. What would the Victorian railway engineers have thought of plans for a 14-lane orbital motorway around London?

It is not only the natural countryside that is being affected dramatically by the pressures of development. There is growing evidence now that traffic, industry and human activity are affecting the atmosphere that we and all living organisms depend on for our existence. It is happening locally, with fumes blocking the sunlight from our major cities. It is already true that pollution can be detected all around the globe, even in those few areas still remote from human activity. Fortunately for our butterflies, insects, with their relatively simple physiology, are perhaps better equipped to withstand the effects of air pollution than we higher organisms. They are not, however, well equipped to adapt to the dramatic changes in our countryside, or with agrochemical pollution that attacks their foodplants.

Air pollution may affect butterflies in more subtle ways. If global warming leads to an increase in average temperature, species currently confined to the south of England may spread further north. But there may be an insidious threat to some species, such as Adonis and chalkhill blues and the fritillaries, which require strong sunlight beating down on a microhabitat to raise local temperatures for the development of their caterpillars. As air pollution increases, especially in prolonged anticyclonic conditions, the sun is partially obscured by haze or traffic smog, reducing its strength. It is already unusual to see a deep blue sky inland in mid-summer – haze reduces it to a pale milky blue. Increasing airborne pollution in this heavily populated area may reduce the viability of some species, even though their habitat seems to remain ideal.

A survey of habitats in the three counties, carried out by BBONT between 1979 and 1981, showed that only about 11% of the total land area had even semi-natural habitat remaining. Of this 11%, a significant area was conifer plantation, with very limited wildlife value. Since 1981 there has been further decline as development has spread. Many habitats, particularly heathland and wetland, had dwindled to tiny fractions of their former area by 1981 and have continued to decline since then.

As we near the end of this century, which began with all the promise of new technology, we find that 'civilisation' has almost destroyed the natural landscape. Although most of the changes to our countryside are irreversible, given the density of human population, it is never too late to seek to conserve those natural areas that remain and to find ways of managing their biodiversity. We can no longer rely on other countries and the traditional view of the tropical regions as a source of species variety – the pressures of economic development and a mushrooming human population are affecting all parts of the world.

What actions can be taken?

In realistic terms, we cannot expect to reverse the dramatic effects of widespread development of this country and put the clock back. However, action plans can be put in hand to protect what is still left, with the hope of checking further major decline in our threatened species. The main objectives of conservation are now seen in the following terms:

1) active management of existing natural habitats to ensure that we retain good conditions for the survival of our remaining species and their diversity.
2) development of species recovery programmes to increase the numbers of endangered species and to increase the range and density of colonies. In some cases, it is already necessary to consider re-introductions of species into former sites where they became extinct, but where suitable habitat conditions have been re-established.
3) to develop strategies to link isolated habitats together more effectively so that natural re-colonisation becomes possible again.

There are already many initiatives aimed at tackling the first of these objectives and developing activity to address the second. It is not clear whether the third objective is practical; a compromise may be required by using human intervention to increase species mobility artificially – re-introductions can be considered to be an artificial method of enhancing mobility. Re-introductions should be regarded as a last resort – they require a large commitment of resources and the chances of success are very limited.

Habitat management is now essential if the above objectives are to be achieved. In the past, such management was not an issue. Human activity affected only a small percentage of the natural landscape. If a colony of a particular species disappeared from a site because conditions had changed, there were other colonies nearby forming a pool from which new colonies could be re-established when conditions were right again. The problem now is that remaining colonies of our more threatened species are so far from one another that extinction on a site is usually permanent – natural re-colonisation is not possible.

There are some important general principles in habitat management for conservation:

Site survey and management plan. Before any work is done on a particular site, it should be carefully surveyed to find out what species are there and where they are located within the site. Careless work may thoughtlessly destroy colonies where a site is not properly understood. It is important to gather information not only on the target species for conservation, but on other species that may be affected. Liaison between wildlife organisations is also important. A formal management plan provides a basis for discussing and prioritising action. This, along with consultation with English Nature, is a formal requirement for a site which is also scheduled as a Site of Special Scientific Interest (SSSI).

Recording. Wherever possible, recording should be used to monitor the effectiveness of any management, preferably started before the work begins. One of the best ways of monitoring the effects of management on butterfly populations is 'transect recording'. A fixed marked route is walked weekly by an experienced recorder, between April and September, every year. Recording is confined to suitably warm and sunny conditions in the middle of the day. All butterflies seen within a set distance from the route are recorded. At the end of each year, totals are made of numbers of species on each sector of the route and for the site as a whole. Comparison of these records from year to year provides a measure of the variations in species abundance against which the management plan can be judged.

The Butterfly Monitoring Scheme, run by the Biological Records Centre, compiles data from many such transects to form a national picture. The scheme has devised a set of standard procedures for this form of recording (see Bibliography, page 135). These procedures are widely used by Butterfly Conservation in monitoring local habitat management.

'Mosaic' management. Work should be carried out carefully and in limited areas of a site. We do not have a complete understanding of detailed habitat requirements for our threatened species. The risk of 'getting it wrong' is reduced by confining action at any one time to only part of a site. Also, species within the site have an opportunity to relocate as conditions change and habitat diversity is improved. This principle of creating a 'mosaic' of local habitats within a site is beneficial not only to butterflies, but to many other species.

Work should also be carried out at a time of year when accidental damage to species can be minimised. For butterflies, this usually means the dormant winter months.

Habitat management

The following sections describe management for a variety of habitats, with butterfly diversity as the principal aim. Examples of local initiatives illustrate the methods used to manage and improve habitats.

Meadows

Ancient meadows are good butterfly habitats supporting some of the less common species. They have a wide variety of grasses and herbs. The BBONT Bernwood Meadows reserve is a good example, with a rich variety of wild plants, including cuckooflower, orchids and adder's-tongue, and also many butterfly species. They are typical of meadows used for grazing and hay-making over centuries. In some meadows, vigorous grass growth is checked by yellow-rattle, a semi-parasitic herb which taps into the roots of neighbouring plants.

Most of our ancient meadows have been lost to intensive agriculture, with fertiliser application to increase grass growth at the expense of herbs, drainage to control flooding and, in some cases, ploughing and re-seeding with vigorous rye-grasses. An improved yield of dairy and meat products results, but at the cost of a dramatic fall in species diversity.

For the remaining ancient meadows, often referred to as 'unimproved', management is best done by seeking to maintain or restore the traditional practices that led to their development – usually light grazing by cattle, or hay-making where that was the well established practice. Bernwood Meadows are cut for hay in mid-summer, usually July, after the main crop of flowering herbs has set seed. It important that the hay cut is removed, otherwise the herbs are smothered and prevented from establishing new growth. Grazing

BBONT's Bernwood
Meadows nature reserve,
Buckinghamshire

110

the aftermath also helps herbal growth and lightly breaks the ground, providing germination sites. Although this regime is primarily targeted at the floral diversity, it seems to maintain conditions that suit the butterfly populations.

Some 'improved' meadows can be restored, but it is a very lengthy process. Artificial fertiliser will be gradually leached out of the soil by rainwater, but if the target meadow is lower than neighbouring fields, it may continue to receive nitrates and will remain over-fertilised. If the meadow had been ploughed and cultivated, then it may be necessary to scrape off the top soil layer and allow natural re-colonisation, or to seed with a wild meadow mixture to restore the floral diversity. Mowing, hay making or a light grazing regime will be required for many years before an equilibrium of flora is fully established.

Butterflies that benefit particularly from wild meadow management are the small, Essex and large skippers, orange-tip, small copper, common blue, marbled white, meadow brown and small heath. The last three species can be found in thousands on unimproved meadows.

Chalk and limestone grasslands

The grassland habitats in this area most significant for butterfly conservation are those on chalk- and limestone-based soils. These soils are thin, well-drained and poor in nutrients. As a result, grass does not grow rapidly and small herbs, tolerant of the alkaline conditions, are able to compete effectively. The most extensive of these grasslands are found on the chalk of the Downs and Chilterns, followed by smaller areas on limestone, mainly in north Oxfordshire and north Buckinghamshire.

The chief threats to these habitats are, at one extreme, ploughing and/or application of fertiliser, which destroys the natural sward, makes it grass-rich and eliminates many herb

Chiltern chalk grassland with horseshoe vetch in flower, Oxfordshire

111

species, and at the other extreme, withdrawal of grazing and complete neglect, which leads to scrub invasion. Both extremes are found locally. Over-grazing by stock or by rabbits can also create serious and lasting damage; although plants may recover from a short period of over-grazing, colonies of specialised butterflies may be completely eliminated, because the continuity of habitat has been broken and the site is too remote from the nearest colony.

There are still some good sites (most are now nature reserves) on the Downs and Chilterns where ideal conditions persist. These are maintained normally by grazing with sheep or horses or by rabbits. Sheep can be controlled, by enclosing the flock and varying the season and time over which they are put there. Rabbits cannot be controlled and we rely more on serendipity than on planning where their influence is strong. In good years they will keep the grass short but still herb-rich, benefiting species such as chalkhill and Adonis blues and silver-spotted skippers. Two things can go wrong. Diseases such as myxomatosis can drastically reduce populations, so that grazing almost ceases and unchecked growth of grass occurs. At the other extreme, populations may explode and, particularly in dry summers, cause over-grazing – all the herb growth is removed and there is nothing for the butterflies to lay on or for the caterpillars to feed on.

Because of the delicate nature of the soil structure and the balance of herbs and grasses, it is difficult to establish and maintain the right grazing conditions and it is often necessary to modify management plans in response to changes. The choice of grazing species is important and the best time for grazing is thought to be over the winter months. Heavy species, such as horses and cattle, also break up the turf on sloping ground and the resulting bare patches of soil allow ideal conditions for germination of many herbs (e.g. cowslip, believed to be named after these favoured germination sites – the patches where 'cows slip').

Butterfly Conservation work party clearing scrub on the Downs, Oxfordshire

Care must be taken in managing these chalk/limestone grasslands. Different butterfly species use different stages in the natural succession from short-turf open grassland through light mixed scrub and heavily scrub-covered sites, ultimately to forest. It is important therefore to maintain the variety of stages if the greatest variety of butterfly species is also to be maintained. The Duke of Burgundy, for example, needs longer grasses with the greater shade they offer to cowslips. Dark green fritillaries need the longer grasses sheltering delicate violet plants, often at the edge of partially scrub-covered sites. The management plans used to maintain these sites aim to produce a variety of habitat stages, by moving activity from one area to another within a site.

Some grassland sites have been neglected for decades and may be covered in extensive blanket scrub or woodland. Restoration of this type of site is labour-intensive, but can be very rewarding, with almost immediate increases in populations of butterflies. At one such site on the Downs, actively managed by Butterfly Conservation working with English Nature, work parties of volunteers carry out scrub clearance and coppicing during the winter months, interspersed with transect recording over the summer months.

At this site, scrub and small trees were removed in winter by sawing them off just above ground level. A careful pattern of clearance was used, creating open but sheltered pockets within surrounding scrub, with a variety of microclimates. The resulting debris was burnt, leaving the ground clear.

Returning to the same site the following summer, the ground was a mass of herbs, including violets, cowslips and chalk grassland plants such as rock rose, milk vetch and salad burnet, as well as a light growth of grasses. Already, species such as Duke of Burgundy, grizzled skipper and green hairstreak had moved in to colonise the area.

The following year, regrowth from the coppice stumps was becoming obvious. Within about five years, this site would revert to scrub cover if no further management was carried out, and either renewed clearance or clearance on an adjacent part of the site is necessary to maintain this crucial variety.

Heathlands

There are two types of heathland found in this area, the acid heaths along the borders of Berkshire with Hampshire and Surrey and the sandy alkaline heaths mainly to the south-west of Oxford.

The former are larger in extent than the latter, and are dominated by heathers interspersed with birch, gorse and bilberry, with some grassland and stands of bracken. In low-lying areas, pools of standing water with sphagnum moss form deep layers of peat and typical marsh plants such as bog asphodel and sundew occur. Many heathlands were once large tracts of common land used for grazing and for a local supply of wood and peat for fuel.

There are several local sites which are typical of this type of habitat, including Owlsmoor Bog (a BBONT reserve), Sandhurst Heath (mainly Ministry of Defence land) and Silchester Common (just over the border in Hampshire). The name of the latter indicates its former status for grazing. There is only now a fraction of the area under heath that there once was, with a total of only a little over a square mile (2.6 km²) now left in Berkshire – a result of years of cultivation and industrial, road and housing development, along with major gravel extraction to provide the raw materials.

The habitats of graylings and silver-studded blues are found where there are areas of bare soil within the heath. If heathland is left unmanaged, heather grows over such bare patches, and birch gradually establishes tree cover, shading out the ground. It is crucial for the survival of these two butterflies and for many other insects (including the ants that silver-studded blues seem to need), birds and flowers that open areas are created or maintained.

Grazing at one time would have controlled the growth of trees, scrub and heather and, where practical, is still the preferred method. The principal method of management of heather now tends to be by controlled burning, which removes the established mature heather growth. Exposed areas of bare soil result, where herbs can compete with fresh heather growth. This has to be done with care, restricting the area of each burn so that species can re-colonise the newly cleared areas from neighbouring parts of the site. Uncontrolled burning over a whole site may extinguish many insect species and may damage the basic ecology of the heath. Bracken invasion may occur, which is very difficult to control. Birch invasion is checked by cutting down sapling trees and selective contact herbicide may be used effectively to prevent unwanted re-growth.

A Berkshire Heathland Project was launched in 1993 involving English Nature, voluntary conservation organisations and district and county councils, to improve the management of the remaining heathlands, by attracting funding for fencing and grazing and some heath re-establishment on former gravel extraction sites. This is part of a national initiative, which reflects an even wider international need to save such habitats.

Sandhurst Heath, Berkshire

The sandy heaths to the south-west of Oxford are associated with corallian limestone beds, and are heavily worked for sand extraction. The main areas of current conservation interest now are the worked-out sand pits, several examples of which are located near Cothill, to the north-west of Abingdon. The area encompasses the unusual calcareous fen at Parsonage Moor, a National Nature Reserve famous for the pioneering work of Professor E.B. Ford on the scarlet tiger moth, and known also for some rare plants.

Although much of the area of sand extraction near Cothill has been used for refuse infilling, some pits have been left to nature, including Dry Sandford Pit and Hitchcopse Pit (recently extended following new workings, now completed). The sandy soils drain freely and have little nutrient content. Their agricultural value is at best marginal. Plants colonise these soils very slowly, and dry-tolerant herb species can thrive in competition with grass species. The result is a very varied herb-rich grassland. The Cothill sites are valued also for their rich variety of solitary bees and wasps, which inhabit holes easily drilled into the sand, and make extensive use of cliffs left within these areas.

Maintenance of these sites is mainly limited to preventing gradual scrub invasion. Rabbit overgrazing has been a problem in recent dry summers and herb growth has been taken off many areas almost completely. Where there are no rabbit populations, occasional stock grazing is used to take off excessive grass growth. Birch invasion is controlled also by use of systemic contact herbicides to prevent regrowth.

The species that thrive on these thin sandy grasslands include all the meadow species, along with the brown argus. In addition, green hairstreaks can colonise scrubby margins, and there is a limited small blue colony based on a large spread of kidney vetch on one site.

Woodland habitats

Woodland, the dominant part of our local semi-natural habitats, can provide a very useful structure of mixed habitats in which a variety of insect species can find suitable conditions. Open clearings and wide rides within woodland are colonised by most of the meadow species. Areas at the wood edge, especially where there is scrub, are good for ringlets and gatekeepers, whilst speckled woods occupy shady regions where dappled sunlight penetrates.

Several of the threatened or localised butterflies in our area are woodland species and have specialist requirements for the structure of suitable habitat. Purple emperors are tree-canopy species which breed over areas of deciduous woodland, given the right structure of high trees for mating and sallow trees for egg-laying. White admirals use straggly honeysuckle in rather 'neglected' woodland with shady rides as their preferred habitat.

Ancient woodlands, with their native deciduous trees, provide the best potential for conservation, but form less than 8% of our total woodland area. Mixed woodland may also provide suitable conditions and even coniferous plantations can have some interesting colonies, but only if there are sufficient open areas within the wood, where the dormant seeds of the natural flora predating the plantation has the opportunity to germinate. In the longer term, conifers and non-native deciduous trees (such as sycamore) should be replaced with native species. There are two main themes of woodland management that form the basis of most plans aimed at conservation of butterflies, namely ride management and clearing management.

The development of a system of rides, wide enough to let sunlight reach ground level for a large part of the day, produces grassland breeding sites for many species and also corridors along which many species can spread through a wood to colonise other suitable sites. Study has shown that rides running mainly east to west, with longer hours of direct sunlight at ground level, are more suitable for most butterfly species than rides running north to south. Rides are also better with scrubby edges rather than an abrupt tree line. In some woodlands managed only for game shooting, rides have been ploughed up to the tree edge and sown with tough rye grasses which need regular mowing. The result is deeply impoverished conditions for wildlife, as well as a rather uninteresting wood to shoot in. The Game Conservancy produces extensive recommendations on management of woodlands, which are very much sympathetic to wildlife and are also of long-term value to shooting interests, but not all owners choose to follow this advice.

The sunnier rides support species such as the large, small and Essex skippers, common blue and, in some woods, marbled white and grizzled skipper, while the wood white will frequent shadier conditions found in narrower rides.

Larger clearings in woods provide a good mixture of sheltered habitat conditions which range from meadow grassland in the centre to a scrub/tree habitat at the edges. Clearings are normally transitional in woodland; seedlings develop and grow in a clearing, eventually returning it to its original form.

The modern practice of clear-felling very large areas of woodland in a single season produces very dramatic changes in habitat structure, both because of the damage done to

Clear-felling operations in woodland near Frilsham, Berkshire

the soil structure by the action of the heavy machinery used and by the very exposed nature of the large open areas generated, and are seldom beneficial to insects.

The most beneficial way to form a clearing in woodland for conservation purposes is by the ancient management system known as coppicing. Trees are cut down close to ground level, leaving only a few isolated specimens to develop as full standards. The cut stumps (known as coppice stools) sprout new growth and within a few seasons, the new growth begins to shade out the ground again.

Coppicing is carried out on a cycle, with cutting of the coppice stools being repeated periodically. Traditionally, this practice provided a source of timber of various sizes according to need, with a coppice cycle of 20 years for large constructional timber and as little as 5 years for wattle construction or fencing hurdles. It also provided a source of fuel, either used as logs or to make charcoal. There are several examples in England of ancient coppice, some of which have been worked regularly for over a thousand years. Woodland is worked in compartments, with work moving from one compartment to another each year. This provides a succession of coppice stages within the wood.

Coppicing as a trade activity virtually died out by the middle of this century and woodland declined rapidly as a result. There are several initiatives now to revive coppicing, for example to support the growing market for charcoal (now fetching high prices) to feed the nation's barbecues. At present, 90% of the barbecue charcoal we use is imported. Active coppicing is a feature also of volunteer conservation work carried out by Butterfly Conservation and BBONT, as well as by other conservation bodies across the country. Although some income can be raised from the sale of logs, this work is often not economically self-sustaining and depends on a supply of willing volunteers.

Hazel coppice with oak standards in Brasenose Wood, Oxfordshire

117

From a conservation viewpoint, coppicing provides a cycle of changes in habitat structure in woodland and the dynamic variety that results enriches the number of species present. When woodland is cleared, the sunlight reaches areas previously in deep shade. The seeds of various herbs, which have lain dormant in the soil, germinate together, producing a flush of wild flowers, often dominated by violets and primroses and a variety of nectar-rich summer flowers.

The fritillaries are very specialist in their habitat requirements and it is becoming increasingly difficult to ensure that conditions are maintained for their survival. The pearl-bordered fritillary, for example, follows the coppice cycle in woodland and lays eggs on the violet plants that grow in profusion on the relatively bare ground following clearance, where ground temperatures rise in the sun by tens of degrees above shade temperature, providing ideal conditions for caterpillar development.

Within 3–5 years, as grasses become longer and scrub and coppice re-growth begins to shade out the ground, conditions become sub-standard for the pearl-bordered fritillary and it has to locate new areas, more recently cleared, for breeding. Conditions may however be more suitable at this stage for the dark green fritillary.

Recent research has shown that the various local fritillary species (pearl-bordered, small pearl-bordered, dark green, silver-washed and marsh) occupy quite distinct niches in woodland, ranging from new clearings through partially grown areas to mature high forest. The number of fritillary species in a wood is therefore a good indication of the quality and variety of habitats within that woodland structure.

Another distinct woodland niche is the blackthorn thicket, which can provide habitats for black and brown hairstreaks. Many of the smaller woodlands with dense thickets of blackthorn on the heavy clay soils of north Buckinghamshire and mid- to north Oxfordshire support colonies of black hairstreaks. The colonies are most vigorous where there are narrow, sheltered but sunny rides through the blackthorn. Management of these woodlands consists of pruning back the blackthorn in limited areas in any one season, to prevent rides from becoming overgrown.

One such site, a 5 hectare wood in north Buckinghamshire, managed as a reserve by the Upper Thames Branch of Butterfly Conservation working closely with a sympathetic owner, has a healthy population of black hairstreaks. The copse has a wide variety of trees, including oak, ash, willow, sallow, hazel, buckthorn, elm, hawthorn and blackthorn, and is intersected by rides with a small glade. The strongest colonies are in sheltered rides, at their widest not more than 3–4 metres, and at the edges of the glade. The exposed west edge of the wood has few black hairstreaks. The more sheltered south edge, with a tall hedge and neighbouring wild grassland, is much more suitable. There are also privet plants – as well as aphid honeydew, this butterfly has a particular liking for nectar from privet flowers. The owner is seeking to improve the overall quality of this habitat by increasing the extent of wild grassland surrounding the copse, which will benefit many other species of butterfly.

The mosaic of habitat structures that results from a well managed woodland is good not only for butterflies, but for many other insects and for birds, particularly the insect eaters!

Woodland management at Bernwood Forest

In the three counties, the site with the greatest number of species recorded is Bernwood Forest, a Forestry Commission Nature Reserve (see also page 128). The atlas survey recorded 39 species here, including 13 of our most localised or threatened species, making it a priority site for management work.

The present area known as Bernwood Forest is the major remnant of a much larger ancient hunting forest extending over many tens of square miles to the east and south of Otmoor and reaching the outskirts of Oxford. There are many other small outlying remnants of this ancient forest, but they are isolated by large tracts of arable farmland and none has the concentration of species or has been as well studied as the largest part.

This woodland has had a chequered history. It was originally oak woodland, traditionally managed by coppicing with a mixture of standard trees allowed to grow to maturity. From the early 1900s demand for coppice products declined and many oaks were felled in the 1914–18 war. Magdalen College bought the Shabbington complex in 1925 and began replanting with a mixture of conifers and some beech, oak and ash. The wood became widely known among entomologists and collectors in the 1930s as being exceptionally good for butterflies, with six fritillary species and all five hairstreaks.

In 1943, most of the Shabbington complex was sold to a timber merchant, although Hell Coppice was retained for its entomological interest. All timber in the remainder of the woods was removed by 1946. The Forestry Commission purchased the woods in 1949. Hell Coppice was not included initially and was scheduled as a Site of Special Scientific Interest (SSSI) in 1951, but had been sold to a timber merchant who had felled most of the oak trees by that stage. Many entomologists then believed that the value of the wood for butterflies

Hell Coppice,
Bernwood Forest,
Buckinghamshire

had been destroyed, although, in fact, most species persisted in low numbers. The 1960s saw changes in Forestry Commission practices, including removal of oak and aerial spraying with herbicide prior to replanting, with serious effects on many good butterfly areas. BBONT bought one black hairstreak reserve area in 1966 and took leases on the other reserve areas over the next two years.

Although the plantation areas became good for butterflies again, they declined in the early 1970s, as the trees grew and shaded the ground. It was only in the late 1970s that a fully enlightened approach to the management plan, based on more detailed scientific work, began to show benefits and the hope of retaining long-term stability. The Forestry Commission is now gradually replacing the planted conifers with native hardwoods and the woodland is publicised as a nature reserve.

Much attention has been paid to improving the value of the woodland structure for butterflies. The edges of many of the main rides have been cut back in several places to improve light while maintaining shelter. Many of the rides have a rich variety of grasses and herbs ranging from primroses and bugle early in the season, through to thistles, bramble and knapweeds in summer, providing reliable sources of nectar. Shady conditions have been maintained in other rides, encouraging wood whites and white admirals. Some of the major intersections have been enlarged to form large clearings. This produced population increases for the pearl-bordered fritillary, which occurred in large numbers using the flush of violets when one intersection was cleared.

A band of blackthorn runs through the main wood from north-east to south-west, emerging at the Bernwood Meadows BBONT reserve. Heavy deer grazing has prevented the new growth of blackthorn near the base of established shrubs, needed to give the right conditions for black and brown hairstreaks. In a joint project with the Forestry Commission, the Upper Thames Branch of Butterfly Conservation erected a deer fence in 1993 around one of the key areas for this blackthorn regeneration and early indications are promising that this will improve the value of the site for the hairstreaks.

Despite the general agreement now between the conservation bodies and the Forestry Commission, not just at Bernwood, but in many other woodlands, recent events are clouding the picture again. The future of the Forestry Commission itself is under major review and there is much talk of woodland being sold off into private hands. This places a big question mark over the long-term future of appropriate management policies for the few precious fragments of woodland that remain in our landscape.

Marginal habitats – hedgerows and roadsides

Books on conservation often place much emphasis on nature reserves and most enthusiasts for butterflies devote their time to these specially valued and protected areas. The wider countryside tends to be neglected in the priorities of campaigners for natural history, which may be unfortunate, as it forms by far the vast majority of the open land on our island.

Although most of the open countryside in this area is devoted to agriculture, there are small areas within that developed structure which offer useful habitats for many of our commoner species. Indeed it is important to remember that most of these species are common only because of the availability of these small but numerous niches. There is a danger that we might neglect these apparently unimportant areas and lose a real asset.

A comparison of our countryside with the hedgeless bare fields, ploughed up to the road edge, of the Netherlands or much of Northern France shows that we still have something to be proud of. We still have some of our hedgerows, small woods and 'overgrown' corners, but these are fragile remnants that need to be cherished and encouraged.

Many roadside verges are good habitats for several common species, providing that they are wide enough (at least 3 metres, preferably), and bordered by a hedge or tree line giving shelter. The reduction in verge mowing by cost-conscious local authorities has been a boon for nature, although an erratic cutting regime can still be locally devastating. Flowers have grown more profusely than for many years, and large stands of garlic mustard support orange-tip colonies, which seem to have increased in numbers over the last 10–15 years.

Disused railway tracks are often rich wildlife habitats. The cuttings are sheltered and the variety of soil and vegetation structure ranging from the stony track bed (often constructed with imported stone, frequently limestone rag), up the sides and over into the fields above, can have almost as much species variety as coppice woodland. Marbled whites, in particular, are often found on these sites, where colonies of a few hundred occurring along a few tens of metres of the cutting slope are not uncommon. Towards north Buckinghamshire, where conditions become significantly more marginal for this species, it is almost entirely restricted to such cuttings, rather than in the open grasslands where it is found further south. Many such sites also support grizzled and dingy skippers and large colonies of common blues, using the herbs that grow on the track base.

Footpath and hedgerow, near Westcot, Oxfordshire

Many disused railway lines are now in private ownership. Some are used for rearing pheasants, some for storing hay bales; some, sad to say, are used as infill sites for refuse. A few are managed specifically for the benefit of diverse wildlife. Limiting the encroachment of scrub is the main management task for a disused cutting and, in some cases, patchwork mowing at a suitable time of year may be required to suppress over-vigorous grass growth.

Motorways and trunk roads with large embankments and cuttings often have a rich variety of grassland species, similar in nature to the older railway cuttings. The Department of Transport now aims for more sympathetic management of major road verges, including sowing and planting native wild grasses and trees. The increasing frequency of kestrels hunting along the verges is a sign that small mammals, at least, thrive there.

Where a cutting passes through chalk, a minimum of reseeding allows a natural colonisation of the bare soil to establish a better herb-rich flora. There are some roadside sites crossing the Downs where small blues can be found. The temptation to lay on top soil and spray on a seed-fertiliser slurry for a quick greening effect needs to be resisted. It is a lost opportunity to allow nature to have a chance.

The 'ancient roads', our legacy of footpaths, local tracks and long-distance paths, such as the Ridgeway, Icknield Way and Salt Way, also provide valuable habitats. The centre of the path is short and worn, with longer grasses and flowers towards the sides, often blending into a hedge or wood. Many of the common species and some of the localised ones are found on the wider paths, where there is more space and scope for habitat variety.

Hedgerows and field margins are very important refuges for many forms of wildlife: plants, small animals, birds and insects. The importance of the field margin is out of all proportion to its agricultural value. Trials carried out at the University of Oxford field station have shown that widening a field margin from less than a metre to 2–3 metres greatly increases the variety of wildlife that occurs. This work is also establishing that there are benefits to be gained by the farmer – the control of aphids is improved, because their natural predators, such as hoverflies, ladybirds and wasp species, are encouraged. Periodic hedge laying, leaving a few standard trees, is an investment which pays off in the long-term by re-invigorating the growth. Hedge-laying is an ancient art and is fast disappearing. Flailing, which is much quicker and cheaper in the short-term, can weaken a hedge and can encourage less beneficial shrubs, such as elder, to thrive.

In recent years, the issue of food surpluses has been tackled partially by policies of 'setting aside' agricultural land from production. In its original form, set-aside land gives some short-term benefit to wildlife, as wild corners develop with some variety of grasses and herbs. However, set-aside status was originally available only on a three-year basis and land is cultivated again just as a valuable equilibrium is becoming established.

In the longer term, the concept of employing farmers as managers of the countryside and not simply as food production businessmen is required if policies of managing surplus production are to give long-term benefits to the natural environment. Recent changes in set-aside policy are moving in this direction. Farmers can now take land into non-rotational set-aside (for a minimum of 5 years) and there are options for setting aside field margins and large areas for semi-natural grassland or natural regeneration. Farmers can also be paid to take land out of production for twenty years, which is not included in set-aside calculations. This raises opportunities to create and design habitats in the open countryside with the right types of structure to suit butterflies and other forms of wildlife.

Parklands and gardens

Parklands and gardens are artificially managed areas which can provide a variety of conditions ranging from almost hostile to fully sympathetic towards butterflies. A well-manicured garden with frequently mowed lawns, weedless borders and specimen plants, such as roses and ornamental trees, may make for a proud owner, but will not offer much comfort to butterflies. Gardens can be designed and managed to encourage butterflies, which in turn add real life and vigour to its appearance, without it looking unkempt. In urban areas, gardens and parks often provide the only suitable habitats for even the common species and therefore have a greater importance than most people realise.

Like all conservation tasks, the objectives of developing a 'butterfly garden' should be thought out. The principal objectives are:

1) A continuity of nectar-rich flowers through the season (April to October) to provide a 'filling station' for passing butterflies. These can be provided in most gardens, large and small.

2) Development of micro-habitats where wild plants are encouraged, to provide breeding sites for butterflies. Many gardens are too small for this to be successful for many species, but larger gardens can accommodate significant areas of positive benefit.

There are several books available on gardening for butterflies and the reader should refer to these for details of the many suitable plants and layouts. Aubretia, dame's-violet, Michaelmas daisy and the flowers of the herb garden, especially marjoram and lavender, are sought after by butterflies for nectar. Perhaps the best known nectar plant is the 'butterfly bush', *Buddleja davidii*, whose flowers are covered with vanessid butterflies in mid-summer.

The butterfly gardener is often encouraged to let nettles grow to feed small tortoiseshell, red admiral, peacock and comma caterpillars. Most nettles in gardens, however, lurk in the shady corners where they are unseen and are also no use for butterflies. For egg-laying they require vigorous young shoots in fully sheltered, but sunny, positions. By cutting part of the patch in mid-June, new growth provides suitable sites for the summer adults to lay on.

For those fortunate enough to have very large gardens, the secret of encouraging butterflies is to let the garden develop into a natural habitat, akin to the traditional 'English garden'. A mix of woodland in a mosaic with open but sheltered areas of grass, allowed to develop a 'wild' appearance, but herb-rich, will give the best chances of success. Large expanses of lawn are not beneficial and should be left to grow more naturally, dug up and left for wild flower re-colonisation naturally, or if necessary sown with a wild seed mixture. Avoid being over-tidy, but carry out some management, including occasional cuts of the grass in late summer and control of scrub. The vast acres of carefully mown lawns around some of our 'showpiece' country houses are barren to the naturalist.

Butterfly habitat creation

The opportunity for creation of a habitat especially for butterflies does not occur very often but two local schemes illustrate what is possible. One opportunity arose as a result of the M40 motorway extension to the north-east of Oxford, built after two lengthy public enquiries and years of heated discussion between the transport and conservation interests. The route avoided the most environmentally sensitive sites in the area, but a part of the eastern extremity of Bernwood Forest was lost. By way of compensation, the Department of Transport, on the recommendation of the then Nature Conservancy Council, designated a site between the edge of the motorway and the woodland especially for habitat creation and nature conservation.

This site consists of a wedge shaped piece of farmland of over four hectares, bounded on the long north-western side by the edge of Shabbington Wood and by the motorway to the south-east. Beyond a hedge along the short south-western edge is farmland. A mixed hedge divides the site into two unequal parts, the smaller being about a quarter of the total area.

The main area was landscaped especially for butterflies, mainly for the black and brown hairstreaks, and was designed by Dr Jeremy Thomas. Soil was scraped from certain parts of the larger (south-west) area and formed into low, irregularly shaped ridges. The aim was to eventually form sheltered, sunny pockets. The ridges were planted up with native shrubs and trees, mostly obtained locally. The bulk of shrubs are blackthorn, but goat willow, wild rose, purging buckthorn and others have also been planted. Wild flower seed, obtained from the Bernwood Meadows BBONT reserve, was sown on the impoverished scraped areas.

The smaller (north-east) area was formerly grass ley, apart from the remains of a shooting butt. Some irregular patches have been planted up with shrubs, including blackthorn. The rest has been left as rough grass. Several mature blackthorns, known to hold black hairstreak pupae, were transplanted near to the butt from their former site in the path of the motorway. Unfortunately, they had to be moved in June and suffered from drought. Some were then were blown over in a gale, but the majority have survived. The population of fallow and muntjac deer in Bernwood is sufficiently large to prevent regeneration or growth of young trees, so the whole site has been enclosed by deer and rabbit fencing. Some of the trees have individual guards as well. The site is also separated from the forest by a deep drainage ditch.

From the start in May 1991, Upper Thames Branch members have been carrying out a weekly transect walk. These surveys have been supplemented with visits by Jeremy Thomas to look for eggs of black and brown hairstreaks. Plants are regularly monitored and a photographic record is being kept of the development of the site.

Areas of coarse grass and creeping thistle, mainly along the fence lines and in the unsown area, are mown occasionally and the meadow areas are cut once in the season. During their early years, when they are most vulnerable, the shrubs have been kept clear of weeds by using a herbicide. The central hedge, formerly trimmed, is now left uncut, but holds little blackthorn. There are some good elm suckers growing up, however. The south-west boundary hedge is also left uncut. The woodland edge is included within the fence of the former grassland area and contains many well-grown blackthorn bushes. The absence of deer grazing has allowed a good growth of suckers to develop.

Up to the end of 1993, a total of 23 species of butterfly have been recorded on the transect routes plus another two elsewhere on the site. Most have been recorded near to the fence line adjacent to Shabbington Wood. Meadow brown and small and Essex skippers occur on the meadow areas in mid-summer. No black hairstreaks have been seen yet, but this is not surprising as the blackthorn will need to mature before it becomes suitable. One brown hairstreak was seen on a transect in the former grassland and eggs have been found on the new planting there and on the regenerated sucker growth along the woodland edge.

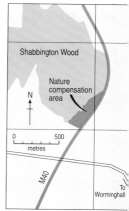

M40 Compensation Area, Shabbington Wood, Bernwood Forest, Buckinghamshire

The plants on the seeded meadow areas are being monitored; 25 species were found in the first season when the dominant plant was yellow-rattle. By 1993, oxeye daisy, clover and buttercup were dominant but many other flowers such as knapweeds, cowslip and ragged-Robin were increasing. Butterflies typical of this habitat have benefited. The common blue population was well up in 1993, perhaps partly due to an abundance of bird's-foot-trefoil on the motorway verge. Small skippers have also increased considerably. The Essex skipper was first recorded in 1992 and was well established by the following summer.

It will be many years before we see if this experiment has achieved its aim but the results of the first three years are very encouraging. It will be fascinating to follow its development in the future.

The other example of habitat creation is at a former chalk pit on the edge of the Chilterns, being restored as a wildlife reserve under a plan started in 1985 and being managed by BBONT and Castle Cement (Pitstone Ltd) who worked the pit. Butterfly Conservation has also supplied resources to support work on the reserve. The central part of the pit has a lake arising from the water table. The sloping sides of the pit have been allowed, with active management, to develop into 'natural' chalk grassland. Grazing with rare sheep breeds has been used to control growth of grass. Some areas have been extensively planted with many different native trees and shrubs including oak, buckthorn and blackthorn to provide some woodland habitat.

Over the few years since work started, the benefits to butterflies have already become apparent and 30 species have been recorded on the site. These include several localised species, such as dingy and grizzled skippers, green hairstreak, small blue, Duke of Burgundy and dark green fritillary. Small amounts of horseshoe vetch occurring on the sloping grassland areas have been supplemented by additional planting. It is expected that chalkhill blue will colonise these areas in due course from nearby sites, as single vagrants have been recorded on the site in recent years.

WHEN AND WHERE
TO SEE BUTTERFLIES

MANY PEOPLE enjoy seeing the colour and movement of butterflies when they are out in the country. However, there are certain conditions that need to be met if you wish to be successful in finding butterflies, particularly the less common ones. In summary, these are the right season of the year, suitable weather conditions, and the right habitat.

Seasons and weather

Butterflies have limited flying seasons and there is no one time of the year when you can expect to see all species. Some are spring species, others are late summer species and many have very short flight seasons. It is important therefore to know when to look for a particular species. Within the species descriptions in this book, the flight season for each species is shown. Flight seasons do vary from year to year according to the weather and for greater detail the reader should consult individual species descriptions. During the period between late October and March, a few of those butterfly species that hibernate as adults may be seen in flight on days that are particularly warm and sunny.

In general, the best times of the year for butterfly watching are mid-May to mid-June and mid-July to mid-August. The greatest number of species can be seen in late July and early August. If a site is being visited repeatedly to observe all butterfly species that occur there, then visits should be made in suitable weather conditions at least four times, in early May, mid-June, mid-July and late August.

It is a recipe for disappointment to look for butterflies in the wrong weather conditions. Most butterflies go into hiding and roost when weather conditions are unsuitable. It is unusual to see butterflies on fully overcast days, unless it is above about 17°C. Most species seek cover when it is raining, although a few of the browns may continue flying for a while in rain. If the temperature is below 13°C, even on a sunny day, or if it is very windy, then few butterflies will be seen. Even in June, there may be a chilly north wind on a sunny day. Heat does not reach the roosting butterflies and they remain deep within the vegetation.

From September through until June there are few butterflies in flight before about 10.30 a.m., and they disappear at about 4 p.m. In July and August, many are in flight as early as 8.30–9.00 a.m., if the weather is warm and sunny, and they may fly well into the evening.

On very dry, hot days, butterflies may disappear into shade around midday to avoid the becoming desiccated and may not reappear until late afternoon. In such weather, mid-morning is the best time for both butterflies and watchers.

Where to see butterflies

Many people start watching butterflies in their own garden and will be rewarded if there are good nectar sources, such as buddleia, marjoram, Michaelmas daisies and lavender, along with some wild areas for roosting. It should be possible to see about 12–15 butterfly species through the summer in many medium-sized gardens.

In general, butterflies are found in the countryside wherever there is a good variety of vegetation, including a variety of grasses and a range of nectar flowers in sheltered positions. Look out for plants such as bird's-foot-trefoil, marjoram, scabious, knapweeds and thistles. There will often be many other types of flowering plant present in good butterfly sites, many of them uncommon, such as orchids.

Look at wide footpath and roadside verges, wide rides and clearings in mixed woodland and steep grassland slopes in sheltered valleys. In developed landscapes, the best areas tend to be hedgerows, wide field margins and set-aside areas on agricultural land, 'waste-ground' which has gone wild, and disused railway cuttings or old roads, for example where a re-alignment has left a short length unused to become overgrown. Long-distance footpaths and green lanes not only provide good access into the countryside, but also often have suitable habitats along their length. The Salt Way in north Oxfordshire is a good example.

The more obvious butterflies will be the meadow browns and ringlets, along with the whites and vanessids. Start by identifying these more common species, and then begin to look for the less obvious ones, the smaller species such as common blues and those occurring in ones and twos, like the small copper. A good pocket book on butterflies is well worth carrying – it is surprisingly difficult to recall details of wing pattern when you get home.

The large compound eyes of a butterfly are designed to detect movement and trigger a response. Therefore, if you approach a butterfly suddenly with sweeping movements it will instinctively fly off. The trick is to approach it slowly and smoothly, avoiding sudden movements across its field of vision.

As you become more interested in butterflies and wildlife in general, it becomes more rewarding to visit the many nature reserves in the area. Most of the local reserves are owned and/or managed by BBONT. They have over 90 nature reserves, covering a total area of over 1,200 hectares. On some reserves, Butterfly Conservation assists BBONT with habitat management work for butterflies. BBONT's reserve guide (see Bibliography, page 135) gives details of these sites.

Members of the Upper Thames Branch of Butterfly Conservation enjoy the opportunity to join field trips to many areas of particular butterfly interest over the summer months. These trips provide a very good introduction to the more unusual butterflies and a chance to learn from others how to find and recognise them. Also, there is a better chance of finding the more elusive species when many eyes are watching out for them.

There are a few sites and general areas locally that can be recommended to those who wish to see butterflies, particularly the more unusual species. The following is not intended to be a catalogue of sites, but simply gives some good examples of different habitats.

Bernwood Forest

This Forestry Commission Nature Reserve has the greatest number (39) of butterfly species of any site in the three counties. Bernwood has long been known nationally as an important site for butterflies in general and for many rare species in particular. The best-known parts, including Oakley Wood, Shabbington Wood, York's Wood and Hell Coppice, remain in the ownership of the Forestry Commission. There is a parking area (with picnic facilities for those who prefer to eat well before, after, or even instead of a walk in the forest!). The entrance (grid reference SP611117, OS Landranger map 164) into Oakley Wood is clearly signposted off the road between Stanton St John and Oakley.

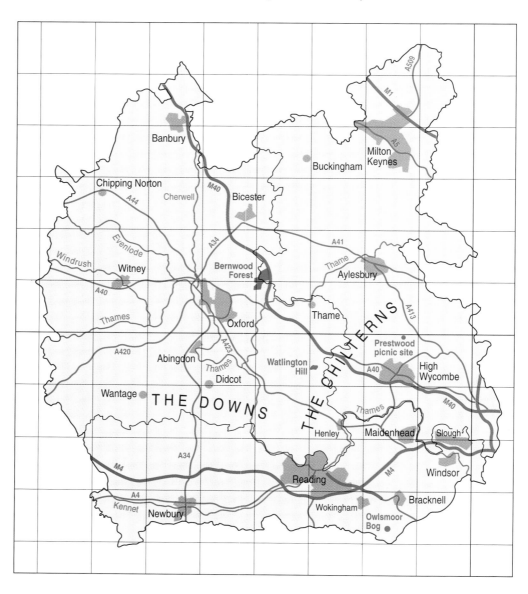

The main rides in the forest are well maintained and easy to walk. Their wide verges have a rich variety of flowering plants and it should be possible to see many butterflies during the summer months. Some of the secondary rides may be quite muddy especially after rain and stout footwear is recommended. The Forestry Commission recognises the value of the site for butterflies and has marked a number of 'butterfly walks' in the forest which are well worth following. There are good colonies of white admirals and wood whites in the shadier rides, black and brown hairstreaks along the exposed edges of blackthorn scrub, and early in the summer pearl-bordered fritillaries and grizzled skippers can be found. Purple emperors are present in the forest, but are often sought and seldom found.

The Downs

There are a number of good remnants of unimproved chalk grassland on the Downs (formerly known as the Berkshire Downs, before the change in county boundaries brought much of the area into Oxfordshire in 1974). Because most of the area of the Downs has been cultivated, or re-sown to provide gallops for the huge horse racing industry, the best remnant sites are those on steeply sloping ground which is not economic to develop. These are characterised by their variety of grasses and wild flowers such as vetches, marjoram, salad-burnet and, in some places, orchids. Many good sites have a partial cover with scrub, such as hawthorn and buckthorn, which provide some important shelter on otherwise open hillsides. From a distance they are not as green as the cultivated and fertilised areas.

The Ridgeway provides easy access to many parts of the Downs, and its broad verges and those of many of the secondary footpaths and tracks leading off it are themselves of great value to butterflies, providing foodplants, nectar sources and a corridor for colonisation. There are various points between the Goring gap and White Horse Hill where there is convenient access to the Ridgeway by road.

The Chilterns

Geologically a continuation of the Downs, the Chilterns are much more heavily wooded, and have traditionally provided timber for the local furniture industry. There are many small and a few large sites on the Chilterns that are good for butterflies. The north-west facing escarpment has several chalk grassland sites, still with good floral and faunal variety.

Watlington Hill is a National Trust site that typifies traditional chalk grassland with partial scrub and some yew trees. It is a good site for a number of the more unusual chalk grassland butterflies, including the chalkhill blue and the brown argus. The silver-spotted skipper is found on the more open areas with short grass and dark green fritillaries fly where there is longer vegetation with shelter from partial scrub. The Trust car park is at the top of Watlington Hill (OS sheet 175, map reference SU708936) on the minor road leading south-east out of the centre of Watlington and access to the site is clearly signposted.

Buckinghamshire County Council owns the Prestwood picnic site (OS Sheet 165, map reference SU866991), due north of Hughenden Valley, where there are parking places and picnic benches. There was a scrapyard on the site about a decade ago, but it was cleared and returned to natural grassland and there is now no sign of its former use. Butterfly Conservation has been carrying out management work on the site for many years to keep scrub growth under control. The site has dingy and grizzled skippers, marbled whites and dark green fritillaries.

South Berkshire heathland

One of the best remnants of the heathland which once covered much of southern Berkshire is Owlsmoor Bog, the area to the north of the College Town at Sandhurst. The site is owned by BBONT and is part of a large Site of Special Scientific Interest (SSSI). Access can be obtained from the A3095 north out of Sandhurst, at map reference SU837632 (OS sheet 175), and then by following the public bridleway heading eastwards from opposite the entrance to Wellington College. The area is mainly wet heathland and sphagnum bog, with partial woodland cover, and has good populations of silver-studded blues and graylings. It is worth visiting also for its dragonflies and bog flora, including sundew.

Recording what you see

It is very useful for your own reference and for 'official' records to record what you see, most effectively written in a notebook at the time you see it. Many a sharp memory in mid-summer becomes a vague blur of confusion by winter. Simple details, including the place name, a map reference and the date, should be noted, along with the species identified and an approximate indication of how many were seen. It is surprising how many of the sightings that went to make up the data presented in this book were casual observations noted down in this way and passed on for collation. Butterfly Conservation has prepared recording forms, available from the local branch, which are used to send in details of sightings each year. New recorders are always welcome.

Many photographers are attracted to butterflies and seek to capture their colours and patterns on film. This is, as many discover, quite a challenge. When you try to take a close-up photograph of something as small as a butterfly, the resulting light level through the lens restricts you to slow shutter speeds or a wide aperture. The former leads to the risk of camera shake blurring the result, while the latter limits the depth of field severely. The graininess of a fast film spoils the detail that is sought after in the patterning. There are two approaches to solving this problem, perseverance with natural light and a steady hand, and use of flash illumination, at the risk of a harsh high-contrast result.

When taking a photograph of a butterfly, try to approach it with the camera at right angles to the plane of its wings, so that it stays within the depth of field available, but beware of casting a shadow over it as you do so. This principle applies both to shots of the uppersides when basking and to undersides of roosting butterflies. The best way to approach photography of butterflies is to try to learn more about them. The more you learn, the better your photographs will be – and the more you photograph, the more you will learn.

GLOSSARY

10 km square A square 10 km in length on each side, defined on the Ordnance Survey national grid by a two letter + two figure reference, for example SP42.

abdomen The third major part of a butterfly's body, terminating in the genitalia. The female butterfly carries eggs in her abdomen, which is therefore plump in comparison with the thinner abdomen of the male.

acid heath A landscape dominated by sandy soils, with pH below 6, normally with heather and peat formations. Typical examples can be found on the Berkshire/Surrey border.

alkaline heath A landscape, usually grassland, formed by sandy soils originating from erosion of rock such as limestone, or from shell sands, with a pH of greater than 7. Typical examples are found to the south-west of Oxford.

androconial scales Scales adapted to secrete *pheromones*, also known as scent scales.

antennae The organs attached on long 'stalks' projecting forwards from the head of a butterfly. Butterfly antennae are developed to detect scent.

calcareous grassland Grassland formed on alkaline soils deriving from chalk or limestone rocks. Typical examples are found on the Downs and Chilterns.

caterpillar The second stage of development of the butterfly. The caterpillar, also known as the larva, is the eating stage.

chrysalis See pupa.

climax forest Forest containing a succession of tree extending to full maturity.

cocoon A small enclosure, often a mixture of leaves fixed together with silk, which a caterpillar may form to provide concealment for pupation.

colony A defined group of inter-breeding insects occupying a particular area within a habitat. If suitable habitat is available nearby, individuals from the colony may move to establish a new colony there.

coniferous trees Trees bearing seed held in the form of cones. Coniferous trees, which include pines, spruce and firs, amongst others, normally retain their needle-like leaves over the winter.

coppice Woodland managed by the traditional method of coppicing. Trees, normally planted, are cut just above ground level. New shoots grow from the cut stumps. After a period, the new growth is cut again, providing a supply of coppice poles, fence posts or wood for fuel (logs or charcoal), whose size depends on the length of the coppice cycle (usually in the range of 5–20 years). The 'trees' in coppice can continue producing re-growth for centuries. Some English coppice is known to be over a thousand years old.

cremaster A device on the tip of the pupa, consisting of a microscopic tangle of hooks which is used to attach the pupa to a pad of silk threads spun on to a stem by the caterpillar.

deciduous trees Broad-leaved trees, such as oak, ash and willow, which shed their leaves each year before winter.

fauna The animal population of an area, vertebrates and invertebrates, including, for example, insects, fish, reptiles, amphibians, birds and mammals.

flora The vegetable/plant life of an area, such as grasses, herbs and trees.

foodplant The plant used as the source of food by the caterpillars of butterflies. Many butterflies are specialised to use only one or a small number of foodplant species.

habitat The normal abode of a plant or animal, consisting of a type of landscape and vegetation, which is often determined by the soil type and therefore the geology.

hibernaculum An enclosed shelter formed from a leaf for hibernation.

imago The final stage of development of a butterfly, the mature adult.

instar One stage in the development of a caterpillar. Caterpillars progress through a series of stages, called instars, as they grow, shedding their old skin at each stage, to accommodate further growth.

larva See caterpillar.

lias Lower Jurassic strata, including clays and ironstones.

limestone Sedimentary rock mainly composed of calcium carbonate. The Oolites, Cornbrash, Corallian, Portland and Purbeck strata are local forms of limestone.

microclimate The conditions of sunshine, shade, temperature and humidity that occur within a very small area, such a hollow in the ground or a small woodland clearing.

microhabitat A small scale aspect of a larger habitat. For example, while chalk grassland is a habitat, a small exposed area of soil within a chalk grassland could be referred to as a microhabitat.

monoculture An area with a crop consisting of a single species of plant, such as is normally found in a cultivated field.

nectar The sweet and protein-rich liquid which is produced by the nectaries of flowers in order to attract insects to assist in pollination. Nectar provides butterflies with a source of food.

ovum The first stage in the development of a butterfly, the egg, laid by the female butterfly on or near a foodplant.

parasite An organism that lives by using the resources of another organism to develop, without giving anything in return. The parasites of butterflies are usually other smaller insects, such as wasps or flies, or arachnids.

pheromone An substance, analogous to a perfume, used as a sexual attractant in insect courtship. The scent receptors of many insects are highly tuned to respond only to the pheromones emitted by the same species.

predator A species that survives by preying on other species. For example, many birds are predators of insects.

proboscis The long tongue-like device used by butterflies to draw up nectar from flowers. It consists of a double tube attached to the head of the butterfly. It is normally held coiled up, but is extended for nectaring.

pupa The third stage in the development of a butterfly, also known as the chrysalis. Inside, cells are re-organised to form the adult butterfly.

Rhopalocera The collective name for the families that comprise the butterflies (the word literally means 'clubbed antennae')

ride A pathway left clear or cut through a wood. Rides not only provide access to the interior of woodlands, they also provide important breeding areas for insects and corridors to link larger clearings.

scrub Scrub is the low woody vegetation that grows up where open grassland is left derelict, and consists typically of plants such as hawthorn and elder.

set-aside Farmland that is temporarily taken out of cultivation and normally left unmanaged, under schemes originating from the Common Agricultural Policy of the European Community.

species A set of closely related individuals that can interbreed, and share physical characteristics enabling them to be identified as a distinct 'type'.

SSSI Site of Special Scientific Interest, a site scheduled by English Nature as meriting special protection and limitations on its use.

taxonomy The classification of living organisms into related groups.

tetrad A 2 km by 2 km square area, defined on the Ordnance Survey national grid. One 10 km square consists of an array of tetrads, five across and five down, making a total of 25 tetrads.

thorax The central major part of the body of a butterfly. The wings and legs are attached to the thorax which contains the musculature for movement.

SPECIES CHECK LIST

The following is a list of the family, sub-family and species names of the butterflies described in this book. The list is extracted from that used in Emmet & Heath (1989). The species marked * are treated in this book as 'key' species having conservation significance in the three counties.

FAMILY: HESPERIIDAE
Sub-family: Hesperiinae
    Small skipper *Thymelicus sylvestris* (Poda)
    Essex skipper *Thymelicus lineola* (Ochsenheimer)
    *Silver-spotted skipper *Hesperia comma* (Linnaeus)
    Large skipper *Ochlodes venata* (Bremer & Grey)
Sub-family: Pyrginae
    *Dingy skipper *Erynnis tages* (Linnaeus)
    *Grizzled skipper *Pyrgus malvae* (Linnaeus)

FAMILY: PIERIDAE
Sub-family: Dismorphiinae
    *Wood white *Leptidea sinapis* (Linnaeus)
Sub-family: Coliadinae
    Clouded yellow *Colias croceus* (Geoffroy)
    Brimstone *Gonepteryx rhamni* (Linnaeus)
Sub-family: Pierinae
    Large white *Pieris brassicae* (Linnaeus)
    Small white *Pieris rapae* (Linnaeus)
    Green-veined white *Pieris napi* (Linnaeus)
    Orange-tip *Anthocharis cardamines* (Linnaeus)

FAMILY: LYCAENIDAE
Sub-family: Theclinae
    *Green hairstreak *Callophrys rubi* (Linnaeus)
    *Brown hairstreak *Thecla betulae* (Linnaeus)
    *Purple hairstreak *Quercusia quercus* (Linnaeus)
    *White-letter hairstreak *Satyrium w-album* (Knoch)
    *Black hairstreak *Satyrium pruni* (Linnaeus)
Sub-family: Lycaeninae
    Small copper *Lycaena phlaeas* (Linnaeus)
Sub-family: Polyommatinae
    *Small blue *Cupido minimus* (Fuessly)
    *Silver-studded blue *Plebejus argus* (Linnaeus)
    *Brown argus *Aricia agestis* ([Denis & Schiffermüller])
    Common blue *Polyommatus icarus* (Rottemburg)
    *Chalkhill blue *Lysandra coridon* (Poda)
    *Adonis blue *Lysandra bellargus* (Rottemburg)
    Holly blue *Celastrina argiolus* (Linnaeus)
Sub-family: Riodininae
    *Duke of Burgundy *Hamearis lucina* (Linnaeus)

FAMILY: NYMPHALIDAE
Sub-family: Limenitinae
    *White admiral *Ladoga camilla* (Linnaeus)
Sub-family: Apaturinae
    *Purple emperor *Apatura iris* (Linnaeus)
Sub-family: Nymphalinae
    Red admiral *Vanessa atalanta* (Linnaeus)
    Painted lady *Cynthia cardui* (Linnaeus)
    Small tortoiseshell *Aglais urticae* (Linnaeus)
    *Large tortoiseshell *Nymphalis polychloros* (Linnaeus)
    Peacock *Inachis io* (Linnaeus)
    Comma *Polygonia c-album* (Linnaeus)
Sub-family: Argynninae
    *Small pearl-bordered fritillary *Boloria selene* ([Denis & Schiffermüller])
    *Pearl-bordered fritillary *Boloria euphrosyne* (Linnaeus)
    *High brown fritillary *Argynnis adippe* ([Denis & Schiffermüller])
    *Dark green fritillary *Argynnis aglaja* (Linnaeus)
    *Silver-washed fritillary *Argynnis paphia* (Linnaeus)
Sub-family: Melitaeinae
    *Marsh fritillary *Eurodryas aurinia* (Rottemburg)
Sub-family: Satyrinae
    Speckled wood *Pararge aegeria* (Linnaeus)
    Wall *Lasiommata megera* (Linnaeus)
    Marbled white *Melanargia galathea* (Linnaeus)
    *Grayling *Hipparchia semele* (Linnaeus)
    Gatekeeper *Pyronia tithonus* (Linnaeus)
    Meadow brown *Maniola jurtina* (Linnaeus)
    Ringlet *Aphantopus hyperantus* (Linnaeus)
    Small heath *Coenonympha pamphilus* (Linnaeus)

CHECK LIST OF FOODPLANTS

The following are caterpillar foodplants and nectar flowers (*) referred to in this book. Common names follow Dony, J.G., Jury, S.L., & Perring, F.H. (1986) *English Names of Wild Flowers*. Scientific names follow Kent, D.H. (1992) *List of Vascular Plants of the British Isles*. Both references are published by the Botanical Society of the British Isles.

Bent, common	*Agrostis capillaris*	Marjoram*	*Origanum vulgare*
Bird's-foot-trefoil, common	*Lotus corniculatus*	Meadow-grass	*Poa* spp.
Bitter-vetch	*Lathyrus linifolius*	Meadowsweet*	*Filipendula ulmaria*
Blackthorn	*Prunus spinosa*	Medick, black	*Medicago lupulina*
Bluebell*	*Hyacinthoides non-scripta*	Mustard, garlic	*Alliaria petiolata*
Bramble	*Rubus fruticosus* agg.	Mustard, hedge	*Sisymbrium officinale*
Brome, false	*Brachypodium sylvaticum*	Nasturtium (garden)	*Tropaeolum majus*
Broom	*Cytisus* spp.	Nettle, common	*Urtica dioica*
Buckthorn	*Rhamnus cathartica*	Nettle, small	*Urtica urens*
Buckthorn, alder	*Frangula alnus*	Oak	*Quercus robur*
Buddleia	*Buddleja davidii*	Primrose	*Primula vulgaris*
Bugle*	*Ajuga reptans*	Privet*	*Ligustrum vulgare*
Burdock*	*Arctium lappa*	Purple-loosestrife	*Lythrum salicaria*
Cabbage	*Brassicaceae* spp.	Ragged-Robin*	*Lychnis flos-cuculi*
Cinquefoil, creeping	*Potentilla reptans*	Ragwort*	*Senecio* spp.
Clover	*Trifolium* spp.	Rock-rose, common	*Helianthemum nummularium*
Cock's-foot	*Dactylis glomerata*	Rye-grass	*Lolium perenne*
Couch	*Elymus* spp.	Scabious, devils'-bit	*Succisa pratensis*
Cowslip	*Primula veris*	Sheep's-fescue	*Festuca ovina*
Crane's-bill	*Geranium* spp.	Snowberry	*Symphoricarpos albus*
Cuckooflower	*Cardamine pratensis*	Sorrel, common	*Rumex acetosa*
Dame's-violet	*Hesperis matronalis*	Sorrel, sheep's	*Rumex acetosella*
Dog-violet, common	*Viola riviniana*	Strawberry, wild	*Fragaria vesca*
Dogwood	*Cornus sanguinea*	Teasel*	*Dipsacus* spp.
Dragon's-teeth	*Tetragonolobus maritimus*	Thistle, carline*	*Carlina vulgaris*
Elm, English	*Ulmus procera*	Thistle, marsh	*Cirsium palustre*
Elm, wych	*Ulmus glabra*	Thistle, spear	*Cirsium vulgare*
Fescue, red	*Festuca rubra*	Thistle, creeping	*Cirsium arvense*
Fleabane, common*	*Pulicaria dysenterica*	Tor-grass	*Brachypodium pinnatum*
Gorse	*Ulex europaeus*	Tormentil	*Potentilla erecta*
Heath, cross-leaved	*Erica tetralix*	Vetch, horseshoe	*Hippocrepis comosa*
Heather	*Calluna vulgaris*	Vetch, kidney	*Anthyllis vulneraria*
Heather, bell	*Erica cinerea*	Vetch, tufted	*Vicia cracca*
Holly	*Ilex aquifolium*	Vetchling, hairy	*Lathyrus hirsutus*
Honesty	*Lunaria annua*	Vetchling, meadow	*Lathyrus pratensis*
Honeysuckle	*Lonicera periclymenum*	Violet, hairy	*Viola hirta*
Hop	*Humulus lupulus*	Violet, marsh	*Viola palustris*
Ivy	*Hedera helix*	Willow, goat	*Salix caprea*
Knapweed*	*Centaurea* spp.	Willow, grey	*Salix cinerea*
Lavender*	*Lavandula* spp.	Yarrow*	*Achillea millefolium*
Lucerne	*Medicago sativa*	Yorkshire-fog	*Holcus lanatus*

BIBLIOGRAPHY

There are now many good books available on butterflies, and the following are recommended for further reading.

Asher, J., et al. 1992. *A programme for the coordination of butterfly recording in Britain and Ireland.* Report to Butterfly Conservation/Biological Records Centre.

Bickmore, C.J. 1992. M40 Waterstock–Wendlebury: planning, protection and provision for wildlife. *Proc. Inst. Civ. Engrs. Mun. Engr.*, 93:75-83.

Brooks, M., & Knight, C. 1982. *A Complete Guide to British Butterflies.* Jonathan Cape, London.
The first full colour photographic guide, illustrating all the life stages of the British butterflies, which partly inspired the presentation of this book. Especially useful for identifying caterpillars and other early stages.

Butterfly Monitoring Scheme. 1981. *Instructions for independent recorders.* Institute of Terrestrial Ecology.

Butterflies Under Threat Team (BUTT). 1986. *The management of chalk grassland for butterflies.* Peterborough, Nature Conservancy Council (Focus on Nature Conservation No. 17)

Emmet, A.M., & Heath, J. (eds). 1989. *The Moths and Butterflies of Great Britain and Ireland. Volume 7 (1): The Butterflies.* Harley Books, Colchester.
This is a book for those interested in the more detailed aspects of taxonomy and nomenclature, and definitive descriptions of the species and all life stages. It is illustrated by Richard Lewington, and has 10 km square maps of distributions as known in 1988.

Feltwell, J. 1986. *The Natural History of Butterflies.* Croom Helm, London.
An interesting book giving expert insight into the evolution, structure, life-cycle, habits and habitats of butterflies.

Ford, E.B. 1945 *Butterflies.* London, Collins (New Naturalist Series).

Knight, R., & Campbell, J.M. 1982. *An Atlas of Oxfordshire Butterflies.* Oxfordshire County Council, Dept. of Museum Services (Occasional Paper No. 2)

Mitchell, S., & Young, G. (eds). 1994. *Where to go for Wildlife in Berkshire, Buckinghamshire and Oxfordshire.* Pisces Publications, Newbury.
A comprehensive guide to BBONT nature reserves, with information on how to get to the reserves and what can be found on them.

Morrison, P. 1989. *Observers Butterflies.* Frederick Warne, London.

Oates, M. 1985. *Garden Plants for Butterflies.* Masterson & Assoc., Fareham.
A very useful and compactly presented book on garden plants for butterflies, with some suggested layouts, written by an acknowledged expert on butterflies.

Peachey, C. 1980. *The conservation of butterflies in Bernwood Forest.* Peterborough, Nature Conservancy Council Report.

Steel, C., & Steel, D. 1985. *Butterflies of Berkshire, Buckinghamshire and Oxfordshire.* Pisces Publications, Oxford [out of print].
The predecessor to this book. 10 km square distribution maps and excellent paintings by Peter Creed.

Thomas, J.A. 1992. *Habitat creation for the black hairstreak and other butterflies beside the M40 in 1991/2.* Travers Morgan and Institute of Terrestrial Ecology (Internal Report for the Department of Transport.)

Thomas, J., & Lewington, R. 1991. *The Butterflies of Britain and Ireland.* Dorling Kindersley, London.
The definitive modern work on the British butterflies, this is an easy book to read with up-to-date information and beautifully painted illustrations. The book is a must for those interested in butterflies and has been a valuable source of material to support this local atlas.

Whalley, P. 1981. *The Mitchell Beazley Pocket Guide to Butterflies.* Mitchell Beazley, London.
Very good illustrations, again by Richard Lewington. Includes about 400 European species, making it confusing for UK use, but valuable for trips to the continent.

Wilmott, K. 1990. *The purple emperor butterfly.* Dedham, Butterfly Conservation.

CONSERVATION ORGANISATIONS

The following are points of contact for the conservation organisations mentioned in this book.

Butterfly Conservation: a national organisation, dedicated to the conservation of butterflies and their habitats, formally incorporated as The British Butterfly Conservation Society Ltd.
Head office: PO Box 222, Dedham, Colchester, Essex, CO7 6EY. Tel. (0206) 322342.
Upper Thames Branch Secretary: Mrs Jaci Beaven, 7 Chestnut Avenue, High Wycombe, Buckinghamshire, HP11 1DJ. Tel. (0494) 444158.

BBONT: Berkshire, Buckinghamshire and Oxfordshire Naturalists' Trust.
Headquarters: 3 Church Cowley Road, Rose Hill, Oxford, OX4 3JR. Tel. (0865) 775476.

The National Trust
Headquarters: 36 Queen Anne's Gate, London, SW1H 9AS.

English Nature (formerly Nature Conservancy Council): the advisory body to the UK government on nature conservation.
South Region: Foxhold House, Crookham Common, Newbury, Berkshire, RG15 8EL. Tel. (0635) 268881.

Biological Records Centre (BRC): A national biological records database managed by the Natural Environment Research Council, collecting data from professional and volunteer recorders. BRC is based at:
Institute of Terrestrial Ecology, Monks Wood Experimental Station, Abbots Ripton, Huntingdon, Cambridgeshire, PE17 2LS.